SOLO AND DUET

including

The Honeysuckle and the Bee

and

Water-Music

by

Sir John Squire

THE REPRINT SOCIETY
LONDON

PUBLISHED BY THE REPRINT SOCIETY LTD. 1943
BY ARRANGEMENT WITH WILLIAM HEINEMANN LTD.

PRINTED IN GREAT BRITAIN AT THE WINDMILL PRESS
KINGSWOOD, SURREY

The Honeysuckle and the Bee

To
ALICE WARRENDER
This prelude to a more chronological
set of recollections

CONTENTS

THE HONEYSUCKLE AND THE BEE   PAGES   1–204

WATER-MUSIC   PAGES 206–411

FIRST DAY

"Well, why don't you?" said she.

I had just remarked that the way I should really like to take a holiday would be by going through the South and West of England on a horse. I had, I said, when young, done a very great deal of walking in those parts. I had regularly walked home from Cambridge to Devonshire, and, later on, I had done several long walks with nothing in my pocket except what I picked up by cutting people's grass or holding horses' heads. Then, after the war, for year after year, I had escaped the urban pressure in a car and investigated inns and churches and just rung up anybody I knew within driving distance for a bed for one night. But cars, I said, go too fast, and have to be driven, and tempt one to go too far. And, on foot, I said, one sometimes gets impatient with dull country, and annoyed because one cannot see over the hedges. "A horse," I said, "would be the ideal thing; a horse at a walking pace with just an occasional trot."

"Well, why don't you?" said she.

"All sorts of reasons," I replied. "For one thing I don't suppose that nowadays you could get a horse put up in this country. When I was young every country pub had 'Good Accommodation for Man and Beast' written up on it. The sign might well still stand as half the motorists are beasts, but they don't expect horses now and they'd be staggered if one presented them with one. The modern innkeeper probably doesn't even know what horses eat."

"Nonsense," said she, "they'd probably be able to give your horse a shake-down somewhere and you could always get provender from a neighbouring farmer."

"Perhaps you're right," said I, "but the drawback is that I haven't got a horse."

"Can't you buy one?" she exclaimed impatiently.

"That's precisely what I can't do," I said, "because I can't afford it."

"Then," she rejoined with the logic of her sex, "why don't you take a holiday on foot, write a book about it, and buy a

1

boys of that time did not mean service, danger, heat, tiffin, polo, or anything in the world but that pension of £1,000 a year on early retirement, which all our elders dinned into our ears as a sublime inducement. Had I gone I should be taking it now, minus a ten-per-cent cut; and a lot it would be worth . . . !

Yes, it was a lovely summer afternoon: a sky of unbroken purity, a light wavering breeze, and a row of great trees flinging patches of blue shadow on the long quiet red sandstone wall of School and School House, and the square tower, with its flag, its clock, and its empty niche for the founder's statue, which his shade has been expecting for over three hundred years. There was nobody about: they were all playing games in the field beyond the buildings, and not even the click of ball on bat could be heard. Hours before or hours afterwards, the drive and the road behind would have been full of hurrying boys carrying books or implements of play. Now there was no one.

A fag had brought me a rug; another a deck-chair, should I prefer the seated posture; one or other of them had also brought my book. There I lay in flannels and a red, black and white blazer, propped on my right elbow, the daisied, tree-shadowed lawn all round. What the book was I do not remember. It was not that summer but the next—my last—that I went through the six green volumes of the old Aldine Spenser in such beautiful weather and places that I can never think of Una or Britomart without also thinking of a field of golden charlock, mounting larks, and a deserted canal covered with lilies.

"A gentil knighte was pricking o're a plaine——"

I seldom open Spenser now; but if I do, that scene comes back. A field at the end of a grass-grown, blind-alley lane; a gate on the right; a push at the gate; and then subsidence into that mustard-yellow field, and the company of Spenser's crooning stanzas, heroes, villains, injured ladies and beasts, even the most boring of the stories lovely because of the music, and no thought taken of the allegories about Queen Elizabeth, Lord

Essex and so on which I have heard about since.

It wasn't Spenser that sunny afternoon. It may have been *Erewhon,* of which there was an early (perhaps a first) edition in the school library; it may have been *Moby Dick, Typee* or *Omoo,* which were all also there. Whatever it was I laid it down, whilst the small gusts of June breeze brought the melting strains of the town brass-band to my ear:

"You are my honey, honeysuckle,
    I am the bee——"

The words meant nothing; but at that distance there was a bee-like murmur about the tune, and a plangency—an augury of life which one had not yet encountered, and a summary (though one did not know it and felt it but vaguely) of all the regret of later years for early years, in a fifth and a third. Then, the tune carried me into some vague infinite; but now it carries me back to scenes then concrete and commonplace, but now irrecoverable and poignant. . . .

As I walked out of London, knapsack on back, and the temperature over eighty degrees, I recovered something of my youth. I had last walked up Putney Hill in 1907. It was just before lunch-time; a toothbrush was my only luggage; I left London with one and threepence in my pocket; I ate bread and oranges; I mistook the way from Guildford in the dark and went to Alton by way of Godalming, instead of over the Hog's Back; and I then went to Salisbury through Romsey instead of through Stockbridge. It made the journey not much less than a hundred miles, and I was in Salisbury twenty-eight hours after I started, having snatched half-hours of sleep under gorse-bushes and in woods. But as for Putney, going up that hill, and having passed the very unimposing portals of "The Pines," I was thinking of Algernon Charles Swinburne.

It was a legend amongst my generation that Theodore Watts-Dunton kept him strictly under control (having rescued him from the brandy-bottle) but allowed him to take a morning walk to an inn on Putney Common where the landlord had

A*

passed Coombe and the Equitation School which heralds the
Kingston By-Pass, I saw a policeman, and the sight reminded
me of the difficulties of recovering the past completely. A series
of pictures passed through my mind evoked by memories
drawn from walks a generation ago.

For instance: When I was at Cambridge I made a habit of
walking home to Devonshire, usually through Oxford, where
I picked up Francis Burrows, of Lincoln, who had been at
school with me—the Oxford term ending a little later than
ours. The beginning of the journey was always the same—
Madingley Hill, with about the only view of Cambridge which
shows town and towers in the Oxford manner, St. Neot's with
its bridge, Bedford with its countless swarms of boys and girls
bicycling home from school to the colonels' wives who bore
them, Wolverton, Stony Stratford, Newport Pagnell, Bucking-
ham and Bicester. It was a pleasant route, though unexciting.
One passed over a bridge, which went over a railway bridge,
which went over a canal; one passed, also, a signpost pointing
to Olney, whose spire could be seen in the distance, but I never
followed the road to it. Except for the few small towns little
can have changed since Cowper (who, even in his age, had to
lament some change) wrote:

> The poplars are felled, farewell to the shade,
> And the whispering sound of the cool colonnade.

There was no traffic, the country was undulating and modestly
wooded, and passers-by were few. Here and there one would
encounter an old pedlar squatting under the hedge rearranging
the cheap jewellery and reels of cotton, ribbons and scissors
which the innocent cottagers' wives of that day welcomed as
Zulus welcome glass beads. Here and there one might stop
for a pipe and a talk with a vagrant, usually a moustached
veteran of the South African and Frontier Wars, confessedly
restless. And, in the heat of the day, there was always an inn
at a road's angle, elm-shaded and with wooden benches in
front, where a waggoner's horses slumbrously drooped their
heads while their driver quenched his thirst.

George Morland would not have been uncomfortable there and then. He certainly would not like it now on any road approaching the "Major" category—cars, motor-bicycles, motor-vans, advertisements and above all a law, which Morland would never have understood, enjoining men to take their beer at certain hours of the day and not at certain others. Bread and cheese and beer at five past two is no longer in the country obtainable or legal; and we have to console ourselves by reflecting that at least we do not have dictators who take away our liberties.

I have not travelled that road for thirty years; I will not say that I never shall again, for I am not one of those who take a pleasure in losing as many things as they possibly can. I may even find again the beechwood into which I escaped from the sultriness of a summer afternoon, and where I took out a pencil and a little black notebook, which I still have, and began a verse, expecting, in the warm hush, the presence of Pan, fauns and nymphs, and finding only silence, smooth trunks, great curlings of leaves and shadows dappling the undergrowth, which was quite good enough. Once again I may see a distant train leaving astern a level row of white puffs, seemingly motionless behind a thin row of tall poplars. And once again I may find a pair of old stone gates and wonder what lies behind the curving avenue. Whether I do or not, at least the road, in the end, bends into Oxford, and, ultimately to the Oxford of the colleges.

There did I always stay for a night, playing billiards, which to the Oxford undergraduates of that day was (I believe) in taverns a prohibited game. At Cambridge the game was played everywhere. Saloons were numerous, and one could openly enter for a trophy called the University Cue in order to be beaten by a little Chinaman. And from Oxford, term after term, we sallied forth, resolved always to take a new route to the west, as far as we were able.

Once we started rather late, intending to walk all night and find, in the morning, not bed and breakfast, but breakfast and bed. We climbed out of the town, remembering what snatches of Matthew Arnold we could, and it was midnight and moonlight before we reached Faringdon, now adorned by one of the newest and one of the tallest of Folly Towers, Lord Berners'.

Our clothing—tweed coats and grey flannel trousers—was much what might be expected of walking youths to-day: the *laudator temporis acti* was quite wrong who, the other day, grumbled in the Press that thirty years ago undergraduates all wore smart lounge suits like the gentlemen they then were but, alas, no longer are. But we had on our heads soft felt slouch hats of a somewhat Colonial type; and that was a day when nobody wore soft hats, and to go out without a hat at all was to invite jeers and following from infants everywhere and lumps of coal from the miners of Radstock. These hats were suspicious in themselves; so was walking at night; so was walking in step. We had passed most of the way up the dark street, not a dog barking, not an owl hooting, no other sound expected, and the last bedroom light just being extinguished in the "Star Inn," when suddenly a shadow loomed out of a doorway and a bull's-eye lantern was flashed in our eyes. "Where are you off to?" asked a deep and surly voice. "Swindon," we replied. "You come along o' me," said the policeman, "you're deserters."

Had we not been so astonished at first and then amused, we might have reflected, made a bolt for it, and had some fun in the dark woods with the county constabulary, which an innocent person, in such circumstances, is perfectly entitled to do. But unreadiness, and perhaps a latent (however deeply latent) sense of law and order, and perhaps curiosity as to what would happen, made us accompany the constable like lambs. He took us into a room, catechized us at length, and ultimately let us go on, very charily. We arrived at Swindon footsore, cold and stiff at six and did manage to get beds in a wretched little lodging-house. We were asked if we minded lodgers having just got out of them. We were too tired to mind anything—even the discovery, half a minute later, that our predecessors between the sheets must have been firemen or greasers who slept in their clothes.

That was one experience with the police which, pausing for a rest on the Portsmouth road, I thought would probably not be repeated. I remembered another. In the year 1907 I walked from Devonshire to London in ragged clothes and with a horrible beard—breaking the journey for a night or two at Balliol where I temporally lapsed into such civilization as the place has to offer. I started with about eighteenpence, occasionally slept in woods, haystacks (it is unpleasant to have a rat biting one's nose when one is asleep) and casual wards, and now and then replenishing my purse with sixpences earned by holding horses' heads or cutting people's grass. One night, about the time of the closing of inns, after a whole day of rain had rained itself out, I crawled into a hamlet somewhere west of Frome. I saw a lighted doorway, obviously that of a public-house, with a bareheaded man standing at the top of the steps against the light and a group of persons below saying good night to each other and to him: "Goo'night, Bill," "Goo'night, Ern," and all the traditional, ritual, rigmarole. "A bed at last," thought I, and modestly approached. For I had over two shillings.

"Can you give me a bed for the night?"

"No; full up."

"I don't care what it is, as long as it some sort of shake-down?"

"Full up; better try the next place."

"But anything will do. I've got money, look! Even a lie down in a barn or shed."

At this point I observed that the departing drinkers, mostly hobbledehoys of twenty in the so-called "jolly" stage, were clustering all round me and nudging me; and then, before I could say more, either by way of menace or appeal *ad misericordiam,* a policeman, greeted on all hands with: " 'Ere, look at 'im, Sam," barged through the muster and towered over me, asking what this was. All were silent; *"Conticuere omnes,"* as Virgil remarks at the beginning of the second book of his *Æneid*—which, for some reason, at school, I was made to learn before the fourth and sixth books, never coming to the first book at all until, in later life, I thought I might as well learn a little Latin. "I was asking the landlord for a bed for the night," I explained. The policeman, a big hog-faced man, shot his face forward at mine, and glared in a manner meant to be terrifying to me and comic to his friends. "We've seen your sort here before," he said; and looked around to the rustics for applause, and got it in a sort of blend of cheer and hoot. "But," I protested, remembering some sort of second-hand, word-of-mouth information, "there is a law that every landlord is bound to give anybody who comes some sort of bed, and food too, if he can pay for it." " 'Ark at 'im," observed the august embodiment of the law; and, in the wan lamplight in the middle of that world of dark dampness, the flushed faces of his comrades assumed an uglier look while, with a suspicion of bared teeth, they let forth gusts of wolfish laughter. The policeman, born leader of men, now assumed the air of a dictator implacably condemning a helpless suppliant.

"You better move on," he said. "You ain't goin' to sleep nowhere in this parish. They'll look after the likes o' you along the road."

I prepared, though soaked and fatigued, to plod again my far from homeward way. Just as, with difficulty, I had elbowed my way out of the little crowd, the constable's coarse voice was again uplifted behind me. "Boys," he shouted, "wot price that for a German spy!" This, as the Americans were later to put it, was "a new one on me," but even with Thermopylæ in mind, I could think of no practical way out except trudging on, pretending to take no notice. Trudge on I did. They followed me some distance along the muddy road, hooting and cat-calling; I went on, not turning my head, and the clamour gradually died away as they faded off to their homes and warmth. A mile or so out, the sky having cleared of clouds and an arch of cold stars come out, I rested under a hedge, a dripping elm above me, lit a pipe and endeavoured to become indignant. I failed. Nothing with the element of the comic in it could ever make me indignant, nor anything in life, I think, except cold-blooded cruelty to the helpless. Also I remembered some other policemen I had met that selfsame day. One, in the morning, a large kind man, who had looked compassionately at my ragged waterproof, passed the time of day and asked me what I was. I pitched, in the usual way, the usual yarn about being a "clurk" pronounced to rhyme with the work of which I was in search, and I had had to take his offered sixpence, because it would have been beastly (and discouraging to him) to admit that I was a hoax. And then, somewhere on the Taunton–Langport road, just about noon, I had been trudging along in such rain as I had never encountered before. Pillars and flung splashes of it came down; my hat dripped, my hair was soaked, my eye-brows poured water on to my spectacles, rain ran in runnels down my neck, front and back, my chest was wet, my mackintosh was heavy with flood, my boots were full of water, and the road at which I patiently stared was a muddy lake with clayey islands in it. I splashed along, empty of all thought, when suddenly I heard trotting behind me and a trap suddenly stopped at my side. Two men in shiny waterproofs were in it, and the driver offered me a lift which I jumped at. They then resumed their conversation as though I (very down at heels, be it remembered) did not exist, and very peculiar and touching it was. For they were plain-clothes men in pursuit of an absconding thief and they did not want to catch him, because they knew him and were sorry for him.

He had been embezzling his employer's money, and had just disappeared with a last lump of it. He was, I learnt by overhearing from the back, a decent quiet citizen, and his temptation had been great, as he had an extravagant wife about whom the policemen used blunt words. Their instructions were to "comb" all the inns of the district, as it was believed that the fugitive would wish to drown his sorrows in drink. Their technique was simple and effective. They rolled up to the front door of an inn with a great clatter and loud talk and took so long descending and entering that there was plenty of time for their quarry to get out of the back door. Somebody would arrest him sometime, but they didn't want it to be themselves; they had played snooker with the poor fellow. Ultimately we stopped at a rather imposing tavern. The two men got down, so did I, and I was just going to leave them with humble and hearty thanks, when the senior one, remarking that I was wet and probably hungry and could do with a bit of lunch, suggested that I should hold their horse's head while they were eating and then go in and have whatever I liked, which would be charged to them. Pelting as it was, and whetted though my appetite was by a rumour of roast beef, I declined the hospitality as I knew I was a fraud, held the horse's head for half an hour in the rain and felt myself entitled to the sixpence (which got me bread and cheese) which they ultimately gave me. . . .

And—for it took much less time to remember (although I was frequently distracted by the pace of the cars or the oddity of their occupants) than it does now to write—as I lit a second cigarette before resuming my pack and my journey I thought of one more encounter with the Force which was likelier to happen to a young man than to a sedate citizen of my present age.

In the Summer Term of 1905 a man I knew in Sidney Sussex became (*a*) enamoured of a young woman; (*b*) determined to see as much of her as possible; and (*c*) bitten by the theatre. He therefore conceived the notion of forming a theatrical company which should tour East Anglia during the Long Vacation, the high motive being provided by his determination to give all his profits to the East Anglian hospitals. The girl, who later became his wife, arranged to come under the protection of an aunt; a number of undergraduates produced a sufficiency of sisters and friends, a professional leading lady was brought along by a Clare man who could talk about a lot of actors and actresses by their Christian names, halls were booked in three shires, and a week after term ended we assembled at Bury St. Edmunds for rehearsals.

The excursion lasted several weeks. The plays we did were chosen because they were out of copyright. *East Lynne* was discussed, and, much to my regret, turned down; but we had *The School for Scandal,* a comedy of the eighteenth century by Planché, full of marquises and minuets, called *The Follies of a Night,* Taylor's *Still Waters Run Deep,* and for pastoral purposes (for we knew several archdeacons with nice gardens) a work in very dull blank verse called *King Réné's Daughter.* Little of these last three can I now recall. In *Still Waters* the villainous captain who tried to make the tempted wife elope with him lured her with the prospects of "the orange groves of Seville"; and the lady, when saved, said to her strong, stern husband: "Tell me of my faults, John, and I will try to correct them." In *King Réné's Daughter* I was allotted the part of a venerable Arab physician named Ibn Yahya, who droned interminable sage speeches through a long white beard in front of the archidiaconal rhododendrons and laurels, while rows of garden-party ladies sat on chairs and waited patiently for their tea. We made no profits for the hospitals. Here and there, as at Felixstowe, where there must have been a shortage of pierrots that year, we played to packed, and easily pleased audiences, but in some of the town halls of the Suffolk backwoods we used anxiously to peep through the curtains in the hope that enough people would arrive to pay for the rent of the hall; while once, at Bury I think, we acted in a vast old semi-derelict theatre to a few dimly descried and scattered pilgrims who might have been left over, with the decorations and the cobwebs, from the last visit of Mr. and Mrs. Vincent Crummles. We learned what it was to stand about on junction platforms on Sunday, and also what theatrical lodgings were like. These last had to be booked in advance, and our advance agent used to go ahead of us to make these and other arrangements and get bills out, usually rejoining us at night. His name I need not mention here: he is now an imposing country clergyman; and he had concocted for himself the remarkable alias of Eli Maggott, which appeared on the programmes, and must have astonished the landladies when he left his cards on them.

There came a day when he thought he would like a rest, and I was asked to deputize for him; I was to go to Felixstowe, do our business and then return to, I think, Mildenhall. When I had finished at Felixstowe I thought to myself that I would like a walk, so I decided to walk through the night and get to Mildenhall at least for lunch next day. I was not ideally equipped for all weathers; I had no hat, no kind of overcoat or mackintosh, and instead of the customary stout brogues, my feet were adorned by a pair of dancing pumps of the old bow-ribboned type. However, it didn't look like rain, and, after some beer and sandwiches off I started.

About twelve midnight, the sky being dark, a cool breeze blowing, and the streets deserted, I reached without adventure the middle of Ipswich when, under a street lamp, I was brought to a stop by a policeman.

"Where are you going?"

"Mildenhall."

"What are you going to do there?"

"I'm in a theatrical company which is acting there, and I'm walking all night." .

"You have no visible means of support."

My pocket was full of silver. I pulled out a handful of it and showed it to him. "I'm afraid you're wrong there," I said politely. He was a resourceful man, and I admit that his next remark aroused my admiration.

"Where did you get that money from?" he asked, in a suspicious growl. My explanation that it was my own appeared to satisfy him; he let me go and I marched on and out of the town.

I had walked, I suppose, for half an hour and was on a dusty road between hedges, thinking about anything in the world except policemen, when I heard a bicycle bell behind me. I turned round and before I knew where I was I was lit by three lamps on three bicycles besides which three policemen were standing, one of them being my original interrogator. It was evident that he had shrunk from tackling so dangerous a customer as myself alone, and gone back to the station with his alarming report to secure reinforcements. "You'd better come back with us," said the senior member, a man with a heavy Kitchener moustache. I expostulated, protested, spoke of charges and legal rights, all to no avail; my depression became worse when I was made to mount the step of one of the bicycles and take hold of a policeman's shoulder, for the sharp step almost cut my foot in half through my thin sole and it was with great difficulty that I kept myself from groaning. However, we got to the station and went into the comparative glare of the office. Nobody of importance seemed to be in charge. My name and alleged occupation and habitat (there were sneering smiles and references to "a pretty sort of stoodent" when I mentioned my college) were taken down; and I was then informed that I should be looked after in the morning. An officer took a key and walked down a little passage to open a cell, while another pointed at a pile of mattresses standing endways up against a wall and told me one of them was mine. I stood and stared in my inexperience, when he exclaimed: "Well, do you think I'm going to carry it in for you?" I took the hint, shouldered the heavy thing, carried it to the cell, laid it on the bed, and was then locked in. "Oh well," I thought, as I curled myself up on it, "it's quite warm and this is as amusing a way of spending a night as any, but I must say I'm glad I'm not a poor homeless man whom nobody knows." I had shut my eyes and had almost forgotten where I was when I heard a loud and continuous crackling in the straw of the mattress underneath me. I sat up sharply. "Mice?" I wondered, and then the revolting truth dawned on me. I had never seen or heard bed-bugs before; but these could be nothing else and there must be scores of them. Feeling slightly sick I got up, beat on the door and called out. Probably they were used to such noises there; at all events nobody took the slightest notice; and there was only one thing for it—I must stand in the corner until morning brought release.

I did; I daresay for five hours; until a turnkey came (the huge insects were by then visible on the floor) and led me along to the little office where a benevolent-looking chieftain was now sitting with a large book open in front of him. It did not take long to convince this sensible being that a mistake had been made. He became almost effusively kind and ordered me a mug of hot cocoa and some slabs of bread and butter which I consumed in his presence. I shook hands, went out, and sat by the parapet of a bridge glad of the fresh air.

When I got to Mildenhall, by train, most of my friends merely guffawed; the single serious one, a person very strong on the liberties of the subject and the insolences of "a little brief authority," was passionately keen that I should kick up the devil of a row about wrongful arrest, sue for damages, and have the Ipswich Police Force turned upside down. I simply couldn't, partly because I was too indolent, partly because I loathed rows, and partly because I was afraid I might get that jackass of a constable the sack.

"I don't believe I shall walk a whole night on this trip," I meditated on the Portsmouth road, "and I don't believe they'd arrest me if I did, and I am sure I could not persuade anybody I was an out-of-work clerk who wanted sixpence for grass-cutting. Here am I, comfortably clad, with a knapsack on my back, and enough money to get me to Devonshire. Even granted that I could still bleat my woes in a Cockney accent without giving myself away by either self-consciousness or grins, how could I, without going into an impossible conceal-ment, grow a shaggy beard? Where should I acquire the right kind of clothes? Could I now, with the price of a bed on me, sleep in a damp wood with pheasants flopping about? And what on earth should I do with my pack and my money, how should I explain my sound garments, all with my name on them, if I really did try to see again the inside of a Casual Ward?" I realized now that I had been silly when I had airily toyed with the idea of sampling a few modern Casual Wards with a view to comparing them with those of a generation ago; I hadn't at all foreseen all the arrangements that would have to be made, nor why I should even have to get two new pairs of spectacles, for they certainly wouldn't swallow my yarn at a "Spike" if I turned up in tortoiseshell rims, let alone the obvious golfing shoes. "Another time, perhaps," I sighed, wondering whether the bread was still so hard at that place in Wiltshire, or the porridge so thin in the Ward at Isleworth.

Isleworth Workhouse. I haven't seen it since I slept there; I didn't even remember to ask if I might revisit it, as it were semi-officially, when I was a Parliamentary candidate for the neighbouring constituency of Brentford and Chiswick. Was there still, I wondered, a forlorn hedge leading to it in which the more experienced vagrants hid their pennies before going in for the night? Did an official still stand over one in one's bath with a fearsome brush, like a witch's broom, in case one needed a little extra scrubbing? Were the wire mattresses still so near the skin, and still framed on such stout lines that they left red diamond patterns on one's flesh?

All these thoughts and many others passed through my mind as, walking mechanically, feeling singularly free, and not taking too much notice of surroundings with which I was very familiar, I passed through Cobham, up the hill under the iron bridge, and then past the woods and along that undulating piece of pretty common which skirts the Horticultural Gardens at Wisley. It was late afternoon, the sun very hot, there was not much traffic, and I thought I would sit down again. I went a few yards in, took off my pack, and sat down under a bush. I had barely lit a cigarette when I noticed in front of me a man who obviously knew a great deal more about Casual Wards than I did. He was holding an unlit stump of a cigarette, and asked me in a gentle voice for a match. I asked him to join me in a cigarette; he took one, sat down beside me, and looked ruminatively towards the horizon. As he sat down I noticed that his big toes were out of his boots and both were encrusted with blood.

His face startled me with a resemblance. It was weak and delicate, but the straight, sensitive features, the nose thin and just faintly tilted, the soft, pointed, prematurely-white beard, and blue eyes, might all have been those of George Meredith—and, oddly, he was also a Welshman. He looked ill, and he was in thin rags, but he was obviously eager to talk, and it was pathetic to notice his rapid changes from enthusiasm to the hopelessness of a man who calmly contemplates opening an arterial vein.

With the fluency of his race he soon gave me all the personal particulars about himself, showing his army papers. He was a native of Cardiff, forty, unmarried, a mason by trade and had had no work since the Welsh depression set in. He was now, as is the wont of these lost wanderers, on the way to some quite unlikely and unpromising place (he had probably heard of it from some other tramp), as it might be Lincoln or Grimsby. He had no hope really; and when, in his soft tenor voice with its Welsh accent, he spoke of suicide it was rather in meditation than in menace. He made no attempt to beg, or to move my compassion by whining; he just soliloquized on, occasionally turning his wistful eyes to me as I prompted him with questions.

He came to a pause and then, as though he were speaking of some place which he had known long ago, he asked me directly: "Do you know Cardiff?"

I said I had been there.

"Do you know Cathays Park?" he went on.

I said I did.

"Aren't those buildings grand?" he exclaimed.

I did my best to do justice to those imposing classic piles which house the National Library, the County Council and various other institutions, certainly the most ambitious piece of modern planning in this country, and, as I disclosed an acquaintance both with the buildings and with the names of their architects, colour came into his cheeks and his eyes flashed. "I am," he said, in one of the most surprising sentences I have ever heard on human lips, "a citizen of no mean City." His toes were out of his boots, and they were bleeding on the highway.

Then, somehow, his whole æsthetic soul poured out. He had only had the most elementary education. But when he was young he had been working on a chapel, and a dissenting minister had fallen into conversation with him about building and had lent him a book. He had forgotten the name of it (I suspected Ruskin), but one loan had led to others. He talked of Shakespeare and of the eminent (he had never seen any of them but seemed almost to persuade himself that he had) who had acted in the plays; he repeated scraps of Keats which he said he had found quoted in old newspapers; he went into something like a paroxysm over Shelley's *Skylark* which I think was the only work of Shelley's which he had encountered; and then he surprised me once more, all innocent that anybody thought of these authors as being on rather different planes, by remarking, in awe-struck tones, on the greatness of Marie Corelli.

I am glad I had self-possession enough to prevent surprise

from appearing in my face or qualification in my voice. I could see, as he developed his theme, what it was that had appealed to him in the works of the female Swan of Avon; she had, like all best-sellers of her kind, so great a belief in the nonsense that she wrote, that it was burningly vivid to those who were able to accept it. Wit my Welshman had none, nor scholarship, nor sense of likelihood, but he was emotional and imaginative and would take colour and passion where he found them; and I was glad indeed, when I had racked my brains for re-miniscences of *The Sorrows of Satan,* to find that I could share with him the not quite Miltonic splendours which he innocently supposed that the mysterious and fortunate few, who had the key to the world's libraries, ranked with *Hamlet* and *The Midsummer Night's Dream.* Any knowledge wider than his own I hope I concealed; and he was egoistic enough, certainly unfortunate enough, not to show the slightest curiosity as to my occupation or the source of the acquaint-ance, which I shared with him, with the mighty creations of Keats and Miss Corelli.

The conversation began to run dry, he to repeat himself, and the sun to sink towards the westward hill; I rose to part, and so did he. He took what I was able to give him with a womanly smile, shook hands and went slowly, his head bowed, towards London, much too much of a gentleman to be effusive in his thanks, and much too reflective to suppose that a day or two's food and shelter would solve his problem. As I mounted the rise and went down that pretty drop to the pine-fringed lake (so like pictures of British Columbia) in front of the "Hut Hotel" at Wisley (where they used to have a collection of albino birds, from swallow to snipe, in the bar but have now removed them for smart tea-room furniture) I was wonder-ing what accident or design could ever set straight such a wasted life as his.

I could not see him, in whatever industrial recovery, fitting in (had he ever really fitted?) with the modern machine; he would have dreamed on a scaffolding, dropped his trowel through the air, been sacked by the foreman for mooning, done his work badly or not at all because his heart and mind were in Paradise, Utopia, Elsinore, Auburn, Betelgeuse and all the other far kingdoms of dream whose names he did not know but whose qualities were of the substance of his daily life. Vision had probably been his only vice; but it was not possible to think of him working as one of a gang or even doing a solitary job competently. I could just imagine him in the affectionate and humorous care of a mediæval monastery which was able to view indulgently the ineffective efforts of lay-brother Llewellyn in the garden, and willing occasionally to delight his innocent childish eye with bright pictures in an illuminated manuscript.

For there is a variety of types on the road. To the ordinary citizens there are just tramps and "a strange man at the door, mum," but those silent figures who, in ones or twos, at intervals pass along the great main roads are of all kinds as well as of all ages. Some are fresh from employment and will soon get employment; sturdy sailors, for instance, walking because they have no fares—I remember one such who, when helped, said he would like my address (I did not give it) so that later he could send me something "as it might be a parrot." There are the semi-criminals who scowl and mutter; there are the young men genuinely in search of work; there are those who (like many modern parlourmaids) prefer temporary work, with intervals of ease and plenty of change; and there are various kinds of "unemployable."

Some are like my friend who looked like George Meredith; not made to cope with modern regulated life. But there are many, and no reform and no charity is going to change them, who simply don't like it, who prefer a gipsyish existence and are strong and cunning enough to lead it.

> We be soldiers three
> Lately come from the Low Countrie
> With never a penny of mony. . . .

That old song comes from King James's time, and there are plenty of them on the roads still, some with pensions, who contrive to exist without too much hardship, with the help of sturdy begging, rabbit-snaring, pheasant-knocking, vegetable stealing and the workhouses, leading the life of perpetual motion without which they would pine. They know, by virtue of the secret signs they chalk on gate and fence, where they can at least get a kettle of hot water to make their tea, a gift which is seldom unaccompanied by food or money. One such, long ago, kept me entertained half a night, and I wish I could remember all he told me, but I was sleepy and warm.

I was walking late one moonlight night and had gone some miles past Totnes, when I went into a wood to rest. To my astonishment I saw the gleam of a fire through the trees; and, on approaching it, I saw a little old man crouched over it, cooking something. He looked not only harmless but attractive as, hearing the crackle of my feet on twigs, he looked up; he wore a bowler hat, had a beard, and was very wrinkled round the eyes. "Thought you was a keeper," he explained as I came near; though I must say the thought didn't seem to have alarmed him very much; he probably knew he could charm even a keeper.

He was cooking a red herring on a toasting-fork; he had a second with him, and a hunk of bread, and he asked me to share his meal, which I was glad to do; and as he chattered away about his roving, his merry gnome-like face firelit against a background of dark boughs and moon-silvered glade, I could almost believe I had met Pan in some modern disguise, a Pan who had marched with Roberts to Kandahar and knew every road, wood and common in Southern England, and every stratagem for obtaining creature comforts that any gipsy knew. He was full of jokes and chuckled freely at them, but the food and the fire prevented me from talking with much intelligence. In the end he rolled up in his old coat and I lay down on the other side of the fire and went to sleep instantly. When I woke at dawn, a little chilly, I expected to find him gone; or, rather, did not believe he had ever been there. But there he was, still lively as a cricket. He invited me, a little surprised that I actually had a fixed determination to go in another direction, to join him on his westward way; when we parted I thought: "There, unless he gets ill, which he doesn't look like doing, is a happy man."

None such did I meet on this first day; mostly they were a melancholy brotherhood and a dull. There were not, either on this day or on the others, as many as usual; perhaps, since it was August, as many of them as were willing to do casual work had found employment with the harvest. In any event dark was approaching, and when I reached Ripley, I felt I must push on, and resisted the temptation to enter either that noble inn "The Talbot" or the little old "Anchor" which went from father to son all the generations from the Armada to just the other day. The seven miles from Ripley to Guildford is dull going, even when not infested by cars coming from behind, and I was not sorry when I got to Guildford. It was a temptation to stop there for the night. But Godalming had been my objective; unlike Mr. Belloc, when he marched on Rome, I had not made a vow not to use "any wheeled thing," nor indeed any vow at all; and though I had had quite enough walking and the pack had become a burden to the flesh, I went on. I caught a train to Godalming. When I got there, I had suddenly got so stiff in the evening air that I hired a taxi to take me the few hundred yards to the hotel.

It was almost ten. I had once been known there and I had no doubt about a bed, as the swarm of Charterhouse parents would not be there in the holidays. The bed arranged, I asked after my old friend the landlord, and was told: "Oh, Mr. —— he isn't here any longer." So sad it is to leave such gaps between visits. But, happily, cold beef was there, and the bed was there, and very soon, glad that I hadn't hard ground under me or the wind on the heath whistling round my ears, I was snug in the bed. I just managed to turn the light out, and fell into dreamless sleep.

SECOND DAY

It has long been known that it is one thing to intend to do something and another thing to do it.

Nobody could have been more firmly resolved than I to make an early start next morning, and I had asked for tea at seven. Unfortunately, after I had been waked I fell at once asleep again, and when I got downstairs at half-past nine the landlady, as one knowing the worthlessness of men's promises, remarked: "I thought you said you were going to be out of the house at eight." Still, she didn't seem to mind, and when I had refreshed myself with a kipper I set out with kind farewells.

As I stepped out into that ancient street, every gable-end and Lipton's window of which had been for years familiar to me, I caught sight, at the far end where roads meet, of a small hexagonal plastered building set in the middle of the road. A sudden idea struck me and made me pause on the pavement. "Here am I," I thought, "exploring my native land; I ought to be sight-seeing; I haven't seen a sight yet; why not see one?"

There was that venerable pile, the Godalming museum. For years I had passed it daily, noting the grave letters MUSEUM above the portal; for years I had resolved to investigate it; and never once had I remembered my firm intention and passionate curiosity when I had had time to go in. "I will go in now," I determined, "even if it means getting a key from the verger's cottage, or whatever it is." With elated heart I strode on past the butcher's, the baker's, the draper's and the ironmonger's, until I reached the hexagon; and, having tried five sides in vain for a door, found one on the sixth. There, as is everywhere too visual on public institutions, was a board explaining that the Museum could only be seen at certain hours on certain days, none of which this particular day was. Baffled and bitter I muttered to myself: "It was bad enough, earlier in the year, to go to Cairo without seeing the Sphinx and to Constantinople without seeing the Golden Horn—but at Stamboul there was rain and mist, and in Egypt I did engage to lecture on literature and was kept busy answering questions by brown majors in red fezzes about D. H. Lawrence and James Joyce. But to visit Godalming once more without seeing the Museum—well, it's disgustingly unfair." I'm quite sure I shall never know what is inside it now. There may be most interesting flint arrow-heads and some of those little serrated things with which early man cut off the ears of his corn. There may be some broken pots. There may be a Cromwellian pike, or some little yellow snakes, going woolly in bottles of spirit; or some dried and tattooed Maori heads, or some Polynesian paddles, or perhaps even the local stocks and ducking-stool, relics of a darker day. "Of course," my thoughts ran perspicaciously on, "the place is pretty small, and there couldn't be any really large things here, like those skeletons of whales at South Kensington, for instance." And then I remembered that even size could sometimes be dealt with by ingenuity.

Long ago I had to turn an ancient printing works into offices, and one of the things I rejoiced in was that, when partitions had gone, there was a top attic for me as big as a chapel, full of light, whitewash and oak supports. I wanted a picture rail and asked a builder and decorator in to discuss it with me.

One morning he came. His name was Mr. Porter. He was huge, fat, red-faced, heavy-moustached, rolling and lumpish in his gait, and his bowler hat was not removed, even when he was in his shirt-sleeves. He was obviously not one of those ruthless business men whose delight it is to plunge *in medias res,* without a little preliminary human intercourse to break the ice. He took out a pipe, sat down and told me that I had a nice little place there, mentioned horse-racing, described his preferences in the way of liquor, and then, by an easy transition through foreign drinks, got to his travels.

He had been, he said, a sailor and a great traveller. There were few parts of the world that he had not seen, though I must admit he gave some, to me, novel pieces of information— as, for example, that the inhabitants of Japan were Mohammedans. Ultimately I said to him: "And I suppose you have been to South America?" "There for years. Know it inside aht," he replied in his rich Cockney accent. "Have you seen the Amazon?" I asked, thirsting for more enlightenment. "Why, yes; been right up it," he observed. Then taking his pipe from his mouth and using it as an aid to gesture, he volunteered all I needed in the way of butterflies, alligators, and macaws, until at last we came to boa-constrictors.

Here he became eloquent. Boa-constrictors, he said, were the most remarkable things in creation; for they were faithful beyond human hope or aspiration. They wedded for life; they always went about in pairs; and, if one partner to a boa-constrictor union was shot the other invariably returned to the forest and died of grief. After something approaching a sermon on this supreme example of Nobility among Reptiles, he concluded with an emphatic bang on the table with the flat of his hand and these striking words: "Boa-constrictors: True-Blue, I calls them!"

I assumed, as best I could, an air of serious assent and sympathy; and then, when I thought the theme exhausted, he leant forward earnestly and said: "Would you like a boa-constrictor skin?"

"Rather!" I said, suppressing a lament over the deceased snake's disconsolate mate.

"Well, I've got a very nice one at home," he proceeded; "I like you, mister, and it's yours. I should think," he reflected, turning sideways, "it would just about go on that there long wall. It's a big one; but I *think* it'll do."

Rising, he drew a foot-rule from his waistcoat pocket, rolled to the wall (which was some thirty feet long) and solemnly began to measure it from one end to the other. Coming at last to the near corner he uttered a regretful: "Tut-tut!"

"What's the matter?" I enquired.

"Just won't go," he complained; but then he cheered up, ran his rule for a few feet along the next wall, and said: "It's all right, we can just turn the 'ead a few feet round the corner."

The serpent never arrived; but though never seen it is still to memory dear. Much have I travelled in the realms of gold, some things done and many, alas, left undone, but at least this may be written in my epitaph: "He had his walls measured for a boa-constrictor."

Wistfully I turned away; I will go, I thought, into the "White Hart" for consolation; it's only just opposite, that most ancient inn in the town, curving beautifully at the corner with its simple gables, its oak, its plaster, its overhanging storeys, and above all that lovely old sign, the meek hart lying with his feet underneath and a golden collar round his neck; a hart like that in the Wilton Diptych in the National Gallery that was the

badge of poor, melancholy, perverted, self-pitying Richard II,
a hart that might have made friends with St. Hubert himself.
I began to cross the road. There was the building. The sign
had gone, the ground-floor had been turned into shops, though
not one of them was yet adorned with that maddeningly mono-
tonous red-and-gold Woolworth fascia which, in the end, without respect to local architecture, old or new, Tudor or Tartar,
will be seen in every great or small town from Lake Erie to
Lhassa. "In the end," I say: but the end is not yet. . . .

Depressed, and meditating once more on the imbecilities of
our licensing system, I passed along the road, with a garage on
my left, and a glimpse of lake through the old cottages and the
new cinema site on my right. Once more I was astounded at
my country, and at the brewers, and at the Tory Party. It was
a Conservative Government which introduced a Licensing Act
which arranged that "redundant" licences should be abolished;
that brewers (and why on earth should they own inns and tie
them to their own brand of beer, good or bad, paint out the
old signs and scrawl the names of their ales—one is called
"Shrimp"—across the old fronts?) should surrender an old
licence if they wanted a new one, and that benches of
"Licensing Justices" (usually and deliberately packed by the
most revolting type of whining, nonconformist teetotallers ever
conceived of by the author of *Hudibras*) should have the
power of deciding what should be shut, what should be open
and when—people who regard a harmless village club as rather
worse than a brothel, and immeasurably worse than a factory.
"The people have the power of altering things," reply the blind
worshippers of what is a nominally democratic system. "The
people" is but a phrase; "the people" in France or Italy would
make short shrift of anyone who attempted to take away their
wine in return for giving them votes, i.e., the choice between
one caucus nominee and another, each frightened of offending
some small minority of cranks whose blinkered minds, on one
issue alone, may swing an election one way or another,
incidentally and in the mad manner of the Gadarene swine,
flinging the country into ruinous war, or disgraceful peace, or
the loss of Empire or any other minor matter simply because

they cannot bear the idea of not interfering with their neighbours' personal habits. They have not dared to go to the lengths that they and their insane female accomplices went in America. Try England with Prohibition and it will go back to Chaucer, Shakespeare, Dr. Johnson and Cobbett as it did in 1914 and during the General Strike, throwing off its back all the England-hating Welsh from Henry VIII and Thomas Cromwell to Oliver Cromwell (né Williams) and the rest. But take away from the ordinary Englishman only some of his liberties, remove his landmarks only in part, and, good-tempered and patient as he is, he will merely assemble where and when he is allowed to assemble, lament the passing of the "Old Ship" or the "Burlington" at Chiswick (which dated from Agincourt, was frequented by Thames ferrymen and had probably never seen a man drunk in our day), complain that the new pubs are not what the old ones were, that they are more crowded, that managers from the north are not the same as landlords from one's own locality, and that it is abominable to have to drink quickly at ten o'clock, but that "they're all the same, the —— politicians"—and they stand it and console themselves with memories of horses and cricket, characters long dead and campaigns long over.

So the "White Hart" has gone. "The 'Saracen's Head' looks down the lane where we shall never drink wine again." That was Chesterton, in *The Flying Inn,* of which Flecker, dying, wrote to me saying that he thought it was the grandest of modern fictions.

From one point of view alone, of course, he was talking; he was regarding, not construction or dramatization, but opinion and power of writing. As I walked, in the heat, along that uninteresting road from Godalming to Milford, redeemed, in one marsh patch, by the pool, near the road to Compton and the relics of G. F. Watts, in which the cows, in summer, stand up to their knees, placidly in the placid water, I wondered about the urbanization of our recent literature, the loss of religion, of passion, of humour, of historical sense, and of style. I remembered that, when I was young, those of us who were constantly aware of the mystery of life, who cared for continuity, who

B

had no illusions about automatic progress, who did not necessarily believe that to-morrow would be better than to-day or that to-day was necessarily better than yesterday, used to curl our lips at Mr. Bernard Shaw and Mr. H. G. Wells, the oracles of that time, both of whom, we held, might have been men-of-letters leaving permanent legacies behind them had they not chosen rather to produce cheap-jack systems in journalistic language. What we would have thought could we have foreseen the present day I do not know: a day which lacks even idols with feet of clay, a day of painters mincingly fencing with technique, of musicians who make cacophonous noises or linger tediously in dark forests of echoes, of versifiers who attempt to astound by fanatical or cynical opinions or lack of melody. We shouldn't have believed it could happen; and perhaps it wouldn't have happened if it hadn't been for the war which blew to pieces a whole generation which had just learnt to reconcile faith with fact, song with reality, and left its children too weak and bewildered to face an age, after all no wickeder than previous ages though its machines may be more terrible than theirs, in which all the easy optimisms from Rousseau's onwards have been thrown into the dust-bin after the philosophies, theologies and ethics that those replaced.

"Lord, how hot is it!" The sweat was pouring down my brows and leaking over my spectacles; well, it was only a mile or two to Milford, and then I should get into the open country. I passed the "cottage" where Theodore Byard used to live, after he had lost his singing voice in the war (a place with a miniature, but real, park, elms and grass and cattle, which, on so small a scale, I have only seen elsewhere in Lincolnshire), bought a whiting (skinned and tailed, and put in a newspaper wrapping) at a fish-shop, and began the pleasant climb up through Witley Common, which showed no trace of the thousands of Canadians who camped there during the war, but was covered with St. John's Wort, the last top buds of willow-herb, and the grey-lilac fluff of thistles. The view spread and spread as I mounted, and indignation swelled in my breast against the superior persons who imagine that Surrey is all villa-dom, sand, golf-courses, gas-works and

Woking; for, south of the Guildford–Dorking line nothing could be more beautiful and varied, and here for miles to right and left of me, were open primitive commons without a house visible.

Nearing the top I blushed. I had killed there—well at any rate not a fox, but a game bird out of season. Once, on a fine August morning, I had been chasing townwards alone in a car when I saw coming towards me on the left a covey of seven partridges. Primitive man arose in me; I thought nothing of licences or Game Laws; instinct merely yelled at me: "Can you hit one of them with the windscreen?" I accelerated to about sixty. It was nicely timed, though I cannot honestly swear that, in the really orthodox way, I picked the outside bird. But at any rate one came down.

I stopped. I didn't know what to do about it. What was the good of a single partridge to a household like mine; how preposterous it would be, since I was to be in town for the night, to "park" it either with a garage-proprietor or a club-porter, either of whom might have looked strangely at me for being in possession of partridges, or even a partridge, before September 1st? The *Deus ex machina* appeared in the shape of a smart, military-looking A.A. Scout with a motor-bicycle and side-car. He saluted. I saluted. "I've knocked down a bird there," I said; "perhaps you might like it." He walked to the spot indicated and brandished his trophy. I saluted; he saluted; then I skimmed on my way. . . .

Just over the top of the hill there was a sandy track to my left; I felt like a change from the high-road so I took it, though I knew where it would lead me. Through the heather I went, drinking in an occasional waft of breeze, avoiding beetles and hole-drilling bees under my feet, enjoying the colour of the gorse, the heath and bell-heather, pausing now and then to look at the wide stretches of moorland and the blue hills far away, once putting up a night-jar which may have had a very late brood, until the path led downwards to a mingling of trees and common and I was passing the Hammer Ponds. Small lakes with that name are not uncommon in Surrey and Sussex; once they were used for the southern, wood-smelting, ironworks; now they are the haunt of trout and wild duck and at peace, and ravens may yet build their nests in the slag-heaps of Staffordshire. To the right again and, after ten minutes, I found myself near the primitive cricket-ground of Thursley village. It is not so eminent in the annals of Surrey county cricket as the neighbouring ground of Tilford, where Silver Billy Beldham played, and the Cæsars, and where the local publican umpire once gave an opponent "out" with the verdict: "Out, the damned teetotaller!"; but the game is played there with much amusement and not too many appurtenances.

The pavilion was shut; the roller was idle; the vast landscape all around was deserted; the struggle with the wicket and heather and gorse around the out-field was still, evidently, not perfect; though it had made some ground since the days when I used to be afraid of putting the late Reginald Berkeley on there for fear he should kill somebody who was gallantly fighting the losing battle of British agriculture. I sat on a bench and thought of the village. Down the hill and up the hill in the trees to the left was the Dye House, where old Mr. Gough, the squarson, used to live, a man who deserved Jack Russell's epitaph of a great Christian and a great sportsman. When I first knew him he was already eighty and blind, but he could sit in a chair downstairs. When I last saw him he was bedridden, had a shawl over his head, and was consoled by that marvellous modern invention the wireless, over which he sometimes heard the voices of people whom he had met. First and last he was as young, simple, sweet, good and universal as any man I ever knew; and he looked, with his clean, full, Victorian features and white side-whiskers, like one of those steel engravings of deceased and venerable landlords, with reproduced signatures beneath, which still adorn the walls of country hotels, in proportion as they are farther from London. (There is one of Mr. Garth in a humble ale-house on the Reading road, whose description of the Garth Hunt was passed on to me long ago as: "Fust come the gentlemen from Sandhurst, then the gentlemen from the Staff College, then the gentlemen from Aldershot, then the fox, then the hounds, and, last of all, poor bloody old Garth!") Mr. Gough had been an

Oxford rowing man and a county cricketer in his day; and very old and blind had caught salmon on his fishing in Norway, being told where to cast by his wife. He knew all about birds, and was ardent in the shooting of some and the preservation of others; he upheld the local Bench for fining his keeper for shooting a Montagu Harrier, and, of course, paid the fine himself. Much of our conversation concerned such subjects as that, but some of it ran like this:

G: So you knew Sir Alfred Bateman, did you? He was a goodish cricketer. He was secretary to Lord Palmerston. But I suppose Palmerston was before your time?

S: I'm afraid he was.

G: I thought so; enterprising fellow. Did you know W.G.?

S: No, I wish I had; but I once saw him play.

G: Most amusing fellow. I doubt if we shall see anyone like him again! Did you know Alfred Lyttelton?

S: No. Of course I've often seen him and heard him speak; but I only wish I *had* known him.

G: But I am sure you know E. V. Lucas?

S: (On firm ground at last.) Yes, very well.

G: Most excellent fellow, and very kind. He's been down here to see me before now.

And who wouldn't have done so, who had any sense? He knew Squire Osbaldeston's riding weight, very likely saw Sayers and Heenan fight, and seemed the joint descendant of John Nyren, White of Selborne, the Vicar of Wakefield and Colonel Newcome.

Once, and once only, I recalled, as I sat on that bench on that hill-top cricket ground, did I send a man to him with an introduction, and that was shortly before he died—or "passed away," for never was there man to whom that euphemism was more suitable—one felt that even Death could do him no violence or distort that gentle smile which blindness had only made the kinder.

We had talked once, in his study, full of faded old sporting books, and I (who do not smoke cigars and seldom drink

On Armistice evening I found myself separated from my companion, and endeavoured, with no great ardour and less success, to prevent a large number of lithe and powerful Australians, with attendant maidens, from pulling a captured German gun along the Mall and up St. James's—at the top of which they left it (me in charge), having discovered that Highgate, which they had originally announced as their destination, was a long way off and (in Christina Rossetti's words) "uphill all the way." Little harm had I seen that evening done; a bonfire made under Landseer's Lions, and a number of soldiers and girls dancing, the soldiers because they themselves were not going to be killed and the girls because the soldiers were not going to be killed—and, when I read the Press next morning, I wondered whether the stories about Mafeking night (also the outcome of a poetic and popular relief and release) had been as mendacious as those about the excesses of Armistice night.

However, some other night that week, when the cheering had subsided and the streets were again dark and solitary at midnight, I was walking along Pall Mall, arm-in-arm with another constable, not a member of my own squad, but one whom I had known long since and lost awhile. He was a dear and simple soul; a barrister, full of the milk of human kindness; I need scarcely add that he did not practise. We had just reached, on our eighth or ninth circuit, the sooty portal of the Reform Club, when a man appeared from nowhere and began gesticulating and emitting strange, inhuman moans. My companion started: he thought it was a lunatic and hurriedly glanced at me as who should say: "Oughtn't we to arrest him?" Happily the deaf-and-dumb finger language came at once to my mind. It was only a lost and dumb Frenchman trying to find his way to Victoria, and by dint of various motions indicating "straight on," "second right," and "bear right," I told him what he wanted to know, and was rewarded by a lifting of the hat, a bow, and as grateful a smile as ever Frenchman gave Englishman.

That was all quite ordinary; but when, under the lamp, I turned to my companion, I saw a face irradiated, as Joan's may many earnest students of Nature. I can only remember the kind of thing it was, and that kind of thing was this kind of thing:

Sept. 8. "How this place swarms with robins," I said yesterday while the gardener forked up bunches of pink-and-white King Edwards and shook them free of clods. A robin perched, immobile and dignified, on a neighbouring potato, presented his profile, not even bothering to notice us. "Yes," replied the gardener, "but it is them chaffinches that is the greatest pests."

The point of view: all birds are pests. But this morning, a grey-green morning with the grass pale with the relics of rain, I half agreed with him. The chaffinches here are what the sparrows were in my London garden; so great a multitude that there scarcely seems room for other birds. Without cessation, in all directions, their white feathers conspicuous, they criss-cross the garden, in shoals, in chasing pairs, or singly, the orchard their chief resort. Sparrows here are few. A robin came for the crumbs below my study window, and I watched the gymnastics of a blue-tit hanging upside down picking for insects in an apple-tree near the toolshed. Over the hedge of the paddock two young men and a keeper trudged the stubble for partridges: I heard, later, constant guns but saw no coveys. Three nights ago there were two pheasants in the garden: there are, of course, blackbirds scuttling low through the bushes with replete chuckles as one approaches. After tea John and I found a worm semi-swimming in a semi-puddle. A little water assisted him; he moved like a swimming snake. A great deal did not; he sank and feebly writhed. A creature who can move in either direction indifferently one scarcely pities.

Sept. 9. After breakfast still cold, wet, windy. A starling perched on the top of the fir tree by the N.E. corner of the tennis-court, damp and alone, whilst a chaffinch huddled on a lower branch. The starling cheeped feebly; I could hear the noise plainly only when I watched his beak opening their arrival, and the earliest primrose never missed its chronicler. Moreover, it was perfectly evident that anybody who really took the trouble, with the help of a good pair of field-glasses, to watch birds for an hour a morning, and do a field and hedgerow prowl for an hour an afternoon, simply could not fail to record things seldom, if ever, or at least so early, seen in his own or even in any other neighbourhood. There was plenty of time. She was well staffed; there was a good little shopping town not far away; Roger was in the City every weekday except Saturday, when they would play golf or tennis; and there was no reason why she shouldn't do a book, unique in its way, about the wild life on her own five acres, supplemented by occasional observations drawn from woods and commons immediately adjoining."

Thus far and rather like that, did I get with my introduction; whether or not I made her tell her husband of her intention I do not remember. If I was in a cruel, cynical mood, I must obviously have made her tell him, and make him so rude about it, that she, poor misunderstood girl, would keep her diary secretly. If I was in a sentimental mood, perhaps I made her begin with secrecy, but only with a view to giving him, understanding lover, a delicious surprise at, say Christmas. All I remember is that I did get to specimens of the diary.

There, for a time, I was stuck. All I could remember of the real manuscripts I had read was sentences like, "Still raining to-day," and "The postman has just gone by; still no letter from M." I knew if I started inventing a procession of flowers and birds I should not merely slip into forgetfully entering the appearance of the starwort as an autumn phenomenon, but put down all sorts of book-knowledge which these diarists, being truthful observers, do not drag in. So I thought I would, in order most realistically to fill in the quotational gap in my story, make a few daily observations myself in the few minutes I could spare: that way I would at least get the facts right.

I did. I do so wish I had kept it: it might have comforted

published.   So I began to write a story; I called it *The New House* and it ran something like this:

"When Elvira Hobbs retired to the country, her husband having just pulled off a coup and bought an old house with five acres on the Surrey-Hampshire borders, her first thought was naturally to get a proper, honest, polite, reasonably cheap, reasonably reasonable, and quite permanent staff of servants. Her next was to get 'settled in,' all the furniture nicely placed, everything working properly, contacts with a few neighbours established, the local churches tested, and her husband's trains more or less regulated.   But after all that had been fixed, and a reliable nurse engaged for the children, her third thought was that, now she had achieved the summit of her desires and won a beautiful house and garden in real well-wooded country, she would keep a Nature Diary, with a view, primarily, to her own education and delight, but, secondarily, to publication. When I say 'publication,' I am not suggesting that she had illusions about vast and immortal fame: she was too practical to think of such things.   But, after all, the world was full, nowadays, of women no cleverer than she, earning good livings by their pens, with novels and miscellaneous literature, so why on earth should not she also, who was intelligent, well-read, and observant, supplement her own income?   However humble the increment, it would always come in useful for hats, bulbs, shrubs and, with luck, motor cars.

"She had read 'White of Selborne' in her youth: she had received him as a Prize for an Essay on 'How I would Like to Spend my Holidays,' in which she had openly aspired after cows and cowslips.   There, surely, was a good enough model! There was no question but that Nature's Year aroused more interest nowadays than ever; even the popular papers had an inch a day about it.   The letters, and still more the Points from Letters, in *The Times,* were even more powerful proof: one could scarcely open that or any other respectable periodical without seeing an article on how to plant ranunculi, or a picture of a kestrel on her nest or a cat suckling a young weasel. Punctual as the arrival of the swallows were the letters about have been when she was listening to her "Voices." He had no idea what was up; and, when I explained that I had been talking deaf-and-dumb language to a deaf-and-dumb Frenchman, he was awestruck. That night he spoke no more; and if he lives to-day he probably thinks that I could readily respond in Amharic or Hittite or the cryptic semaphoring of the tictac men to whomsoever might accost me.

That is, of course, harking back; I was talking about Dartford Warblers. The point is, that my ornithologist friend looked almost as astounded when I said: "Well, if you want to see Dartford Warblers, you've only to come down to me and I can show you any number any day of the week." "Do you really mean that, Squire?" he asked, in that solemn way that truly earnest observers here. "Of course I do," I protested; "come down to-morrow if you like. I'll book you a room at the local pub for two nights and put you on to a man who can tell you exactly where they are to be found." "Right!" he said.

I did. He went to Mr. Gough. He went to the Common. Through his glasses he watched several pairs all day; and I, also with glasses, have been there time and time again and never seen a thing except rabbits and snakes.

That is probably the fate of countless country-lovers who endeavour to make valuable and exciting notes about wild life like White, or characters, customs and seasons like Miss Mitford; the diaries are kept, and turn out to be, in the worst sense of the word, common-place books. Sitting on that Thursley bench and thinking of when I lived within three miles of the place, I remembered how one day I had come back to my house and garden after a day's reading for a publisher; the books perused had included no fewer than three country diaries, written by women, and of so outrageous a banality that even had I recorded my own rural observations they could not have been so devoid of interest. Alone, after dinner, over my fire, I tried, not without sympathy, to envisage the type of person who could be so eager to keep country diaries and so ignorant as not to know what would have a chance of being

B*

"Earth will grow worse ere men redeem it,
And wars more evil ere all wars cease."

At Petersfield I turned right, along that narrow, hilly, rustic road to Winchester which is so much quieter and prettier than the main road through Alton. I was but a mile or two past Petersfield, and going slowly up a hill through high thick woods, when I heard a rustle to my left, and there, staring me in the face, poised ready to disappear in a flash, was a thing I had never seen, alive, so close before. It was a fox, his mask lifted straight at me, his glowing amber eyes with their pin-point pupils glaring at me like a mixture of searchlight and gimlet. For several seconds we stared at each other, fear, cunning and courage in his heart, a sudden foolish desire to make friends in mine, to pat him and say "Good fox!" He was there; then, in an instant, he had slunk out of sight to resume his far from vegetarian career. "Blood on his pads," I thought, "and blood on my hands, and that of all our race, not least those members of it who refuse to face facts, and pretend that all the world is the same, and assume that if some of us behave like sheep the rest will stop being wolves." The usual tangle of thoughts followed, as I plodded on noticing neither the landscape nor the passing cars—the heresy of thinking man not a separate thing from animals—was nationalism worth it—how far is climate irresistible—is peace worth mongrelism of race—can it be secured otherwise—how far was the Frenchman of 1789 right when he said that the Prussian was a born soldier and war was to him a national industry—and memories of Germany in 1914, the subtle propaganda about Russia, the vulgarity of Berlin, the ugliness of the Reichstag members, the German professor who lent me £20 to get home with and was repaid in time—August 4th—the four years' dreary massacre—and Mr. Bonar Law welcoming the first Russian revolution with:

"Bliss was it in that dawn to be alive,
But to be young was very heaven!"

which led me once again to that solitary habit of brooding over the revolutions of history, pre-history and the early slime,

Winwood Reade's haunting and horrible *Martyrdom of Man* and the problem of the existence of Evil—which is the end of all such thoughts and leaves a man stranded unless he has the help of a Church without or the finger of God within, and must burden him at times whatever his faith and his charity.

Sharply I pulled myself together: "You're getting tired," I muttered to myself, "that's what's wrong with you. You came here to get away from your thoughts, not to indulge in morbid broodings. Stop this squirrel-in-a-cage business. Use the Free Will in which you so firmly believe and think of something else."

It was all like a voice speaking aloud inside me. It even tried to make jokes. "Think about cricket, for instance! You ought to be able to think of it easily enough, considering that that bowler broke your right forefinger on Saturday; it's bound up and aching, and you won't be able to use or move it for a month. Probably," went on my genial comforter, "it will be crooked and useless for the rest of your life, and you'll always have to do up buttons and laces with your left hand." I *was* getting tired, and no memories of greensward, stricken fields, luncheon tents, deck-chairs under elms, blazers, champagne cup, summer frocks and victories off the last ball of the last over would come; had I been able to think of cricket at all it would only have been about dropped catches and wet afternoons in cold pavilions. "The sun is sinking through the trees," the voice went on, "and the sky is untarnished pearl. 'Look on the West,' as Housman says." "He doesn't," I grumbled back, "he says 'Look *not* on the West.'" "Have it your own way," replied the voice, "if you don't want to be cheered up, you needn't."

So I went on not thinking at all, except that blisters seemed to be forming on the balls of my big toes, that my back was aching, that my knees were not so taut as they had been, and that I should like to lie down—though I dared not—for fear of increasing stiffness and a bedless night in the dark. Chin down, mechanically, I went on, until, surprisingly, I came suddenly on the cross-roads and an inn. "A bed at last," I thought; "I've done thirty miles and I've earned it." I went in and asked. They were very kind, but they were full up. I ordered a drink. "Probably," they said, "if you turn left, you'll be able to get a bed at the 'Dog and Pheasant,' a couple of miles on." It was nine o'clock and the light late. Time, and the braggadocio of a townish-looking young man who boasted to his experienced elders of his triumphs with poultry farming and market gardening, drove me rapidly out in the faint hope of a bus.

I asked the pleasant A.A. man about buses, but all he could suggest was that if I walked on some passing driver might offer me a lift. I said good night and doggedly, if slowly, walked on in the fading twilight, a little chilled by weariness, and occcasionally counting my steps up to a hundred in order to pass the time. Darker and darker it grew, and nothing passed but fast cars going the wrong way, but it seemed more like an hour than half an hour before I found myself in front of the "Dog."

Yellow light streamed from the open doorway, and a cheerful noise of pre-closing hour's conversation. "Thank God I may get a bed at last," I thought, stepped through the door, and, before I had got any farther saw advancing towards me, tankard in hand, the beaming round face and burly figure of my old friend Aubrey Robinson. Out shot his free hand: "What will you have?" he demanded, heartily.

For a moment I forgot thirst, bed, fatigue, knapsack and blisters in utter astonishment at his sang-froid. I knew he lived in Hampshire now, but not where; he could not have had the slightest notion that I was within a hundred miles; we had not met since the last Newbury Races; it flashed through my mind that this was the sort of man who, without preliminary curiosity, would have addressed a returning Rip Van Winkle with "I say, old fellow, I can tell you where you can get your beard trimmed."

"What will you have?" he asked, with the air of a man whose next proceedings would be to introduce me to his friends and suggest a game of darts. "An armchair, if there is one," I groaned. "Oh, that's easy," he assured me, and pushed me through to a little back-parlour, where I discarded my gear and fell back into aching comfort. "I say, Fred!" he called; and got what we wanted. "Where are you sleeping to-night?" was his next enquiry.

"Here, if I can. I'm walking."

"So it seems. Why not have a bed at my place?"

"I'd love one if it isn't too far to walk."

"Just round the corner, and I've got the car here. I can only offer you some cold bacon."

"The two things I want," I said, glowing with gratitude, "apart from a deep chair and a bed."

"Indeed yes," thought I, as I crept into a car whose antiquity even darkness could not conceal. I was rather cold but very stiff, and warmth would soon unbend me. As for cold bacon, call it that or pickled pork, what better food is there at any time of the day, preferably with potatoes, fried or boiled, and tomatoes, with English Cheddar, butter, bread and more tomatoes to follow? I have not eaten rats, mice, snakes, or elephant's feet or any of the fauna of Africa; the humble best I can do in the exotic way is horse-meat, sea-weed, sharks' fins, bird's-nest soup, frogs' legs (eaten on the *Olympic* after she had called at Cherbourg for passengers, mails, frogs and snails), reindeer (eaten at Upsala and in Helsingfors), terrapin soup and raw canvasback duck (eaten in Baltimore), tinned Canadian salmon (eaten in Samaria), and hot roast kangaroo, with pineapple chunks and their syrup, which, in 1910, made me very sick at a small Rotterdam hotel. Nightingales' tongues in aspic; peacocks, swans and bustards went out before my time. Of things not so exotic, but mostly expensive there are many familiar and, at moments of delicacy or connoisseurship, excellent: as truffles, *pâté-en-croûte,* caviare, asparagus, stuffed olives, sole *volt-au-vent,* sole *délice,* sole (or, for that matter, fresh mackerel or herring) bonne femme, haddock Sovrani, cold grouse, cold partridge, cold quails, cheese soufflé, mushrooms, and ten thousand other viands. But also there are stuffed roast veal, porterhouse steaks, boiled salt beef with dumplings, carrots, mashed turnips and potatoes in their jackets and white sauce, duck and green peas, goose. . . . I came suddenly out of this dizzy reverie about food, induced by heat and hunger, as the car jolted through a gateless gateway, up a rutted drive and came to a stop in front of a creeper-draped Elizabethan porch, the door in which opened at once. "Here we are," said Aubrey, "get out if you can manage it."

I got out amid the barking of many dogs from barns in the background. My things were taken from me. I was led upstairs and shown my bedroom and the bathroom. I came down into the sitting-room, was dumped into a deep arm-chair, and was informed that Sally would have supper ready in ten minutes. Aubrey went off to help with the preparations while I lit a cigarette and looked around me.

All his old treasures were there; the worn comfortable furniture, the prints of the ancient race-horses being proudly exhibited by dukes, marquises, trainers and jockeys long dead, and the strange litter of books. The desk behind my left shoulder was piled with papers and in a little table book-rack I could see the *Oxford Book of English Verse* and diverse works on food and gardening, and two deep in the shelves was the odd assortment he had had in his other house of Shelley and Pierce Egan, Verlaine and *The Sporting Magazine*, Baudelaire, Coventry Patmore, Beckford, Pitcher, Nimrod, the Druid and Ruff's *Guide to the Turf*, with hundreds more. Thinking what an agreeable dinner-party might be selected from Aubrey's heroes, I pulled out the *Life of John Porter*, but had read only a few pages when he appeared, beaming and rubbing his hands, to say that supper was ready and did I mind having it in the kitchen? Far from it.

The meal I need not describe; conversation, until it was finished, was at a discount. When we had done we retired again to the sitting-room study, drew two arm-chairs to the fire-place and, with a bottle of claret between us, began to inform each other of what we had been doing since we last met. The meal and the warmth ought to have made me sleepy, but they had the opposite effect, and I was soon being instructed, as often before, concerning the descendants of Eclipse and Herod, the stable of the Duke of Cumberland, Hermit's Year, Lord Hastings and Mr. Chaplin, Ormonde, Sceptre, as well as a whole world of bygone rascality on the part of owners, jockeys, bookies and punters. How glad we both were that all this crookedness had existed in order that it should leave funny stories behind it! It is a strange thing that men who would not dream of frequenting the society of a known sharper would be miserable if they were told that the whole type of low race-train frequenters was to be obliterated to-morrow; they would feel rather as though one were told that Dickens's novels were henceforth to be published only in expurgated editions with all the bad, coarse, grubby, dissipated and grotesque people left out. scores of anecdotes I heard, and many dignoses of the breed, build, pace, staying powers, virtues and foibles of living race-horses. We had reached a sentimental union on Brown Jack and both stopped to look into the fire-place to recover glimpses of the glorious finishes of Donoghue on that lovable old animal, when my eyes wandered to the mantelpiece. "Good Lord," I said, "it's two o'clock."

"What of that?" he exclaimed, with a look of real bewilderment on his face. Then awaking to the astounding truth, he shook his head, shot out his hand to the bottle, filled two glasses and observed: "Nonsense, the night is still young." "It's no good, old thing," I said, "I'm longing for bed. I simply must go up in five minutes."

His normal disapproval of non-stayers showed in his face. "My God!" he said. "I'd love to talk a whole night another time," I went on apologetically, "but I've got to cover some ground to-morrow."

He rose and went to a side-table to light two candles. "It all seems very silly to me," he murmured, "why on earth can't you lie in bed in the morning, and then run over to Alresford to see George in the afternoon, and then come back and stay the night?"

"Duty, my lad," I said, and followed him up the steep staircase and parted after he had once more seen that everything was all right. The bedroom was vast, and the largest four-poster I have ever seen lived up to it: canopy, dark thin mahogany posts, blue head and corner curtains and valences, and room enough in it for four. I was in bed in half a minute, and for a minute more luxuriated in the softness and peace, the dim reflection of yellow light on frames and glass, thought of Lady Macbeth's candle, and then blew the light out. Momentarily I was aware that the moon was up, and that shadows of diamond panes and leaves from the casement were silhouetted on the wall to my left. Then a great billow of sleep came over me and I did not even dream.

THIRD DAY

I was half-awake, and blinking to the brilliant sunshine, puzzled by the unfamiliar room and beginning to reconstruct the evening before with a view to discovering where I was, when there was a knock at the door and full enlightenment came. It was Aubrey, cheerful and well-soaped, wearing a very florid red silk dressing-gown and carrying an equally florid blue one which he dropped on the bed. I said I would like some tea, and he called down the stairs: "Sally, our visitor would like some tea," and at once and imperturbably resumed where he had left off with: "Well, now, of course you're staying over to-night, and will run over and see George this afternoon."

"I really *can't*, Aubrey," I said.

"Of course you will," he repeated, with friendly contempt. "Would you like breakfast in bed?"

"Certainly not," I replied hardily. "I'll stuff some paper in my shoes, soap my blisters, and get on to Winchester as soon as I've had breakfast. You don't seem to understand I'm on a walking tour."

"Well, you can walk to-morrow, can't you!" he ejaculated. "Would you like some eggs or will you carry on with the cold bacon?"

"Cold bacon for me."

"Well, sing out when you're nearly ready and we'll make the coffee."

When I got down he was ready with another opening.

"You'd much better take a day off to-day," he said. "We can see George this afternoon, and it's just occurred to me you'd be sure to like to run over and see the 'Tichborne Arms' this morning."

"Let's talk about it after breakfast," I said, as I helped myself to coffee, quietly resolved on no account whatever to change my decision to cover a decent distance that day. The last temptation, though, I must admit, was a real one, for the little inn at Tichborne meant a great deal to me.

Suppose, about 1906, a man now in his twenties were suddenly to encounter, in a remote Kentish huddle of cottages, with an ancient church and an ancestral park, a shy inn, thatched, dormered, covered with roses, benches in a little garden in front of it, a great heraldic signboard hanging over it, and written on the lintel: "Frank Woolley, licensed to sell wines, spirits, beer and tobacco." His impression would be much the same as that which was made upon men of my generation in the post-war years when they visited the exquisite and secluded village of Tichborne and found Maurice Read in charge both of the inn and of the cricket ground. One of the most polished bats—he was also a wily bowler—who ever played for Surrey, he played for England both here and in Australia, but retired early, in the 'nineties, when Sir Joseph Tichborne offered him the job of looking after his private ground. There, for more than thirty years, he was a kind of secondary king of the place and, after his old master died, a perfect host both on and off the field. The inn was a minor interest, though, in his quiet way, he loved seeing natives and visitors foregathering in bar and courtyard for beer and laughter in the evenings after matches were over. The ground was his passion; in the early morning and at twilight, whenever he could, he would steal up to it looking for the least blemish in wicket and outfield. And, to the last, he himself played in his peaceful corner, against local sides and men on holiday, a straight bat to the end and, in his late sixties, a beautiful judge of a run and a wary fielder.

On cricketing days and others I had often talked to him, in company and alone. The last time I had seen him was in Winchester Hospital, a few days before he died of a wasting internal disease. There he lay, tired, faintly smiling, uncomname for horse, mare, colt, filly or gelding.) "James's Keepings, or Sutton's Improved Reading."

I couldn't adjust. I turned to Aubrey and stammered: "What on earth are they talking about?"

Aubrey's face had gone red. His tankard flourished in the air. His eyes closed, his mouth opened, and chuckles worthy of Sir Toby Belch rose from the depths of his throat. With bursts of chuckling coming between every word, he managed to say: "Dear old soul, they're not talking about horses, they're talking about onions." He summoned all within sight to a drink to my health. I was greatly embarrassed, but I hope that I carried it off.

I had had enough of this place, and wanted to get on. "What about that bus you mentioned?" I enquired.

"There isn't another bus for two hours, and if you wait for that you'll have to spend the last hour waiting outside on the gravel," replied Aubrey, commiseratingly.

"But you said there was a bus!" I reminded him, angrily.

"So there was," he said. "Didn't you hear it come up and go away half an hour ago? Didn't you see those two chaps in plus-fours rush out to catch it? As usual, I suppose, you were deep in conversation."

It was one o'clock. My whole programme for the day had been spoilt. There, on the floor in the corner, was my knapsack, but there, outside, was the car. "Look here," he said, "you'd much better come back to the farm to lunch. I've got some fish on board, and, if you really must, you can walk back to Winchester in the cool of the evening and sleep at the 'God Begot.'"

Through my head there ran some rhymes which I had written long ago and never printed, and which had a refrain beginning "Sheep as a Lamb, Sheep as a Lamb." "No more friends on this journey, I sincerely hope," was my next reflection; but aloud I said: "All right, Aubrey, it won't make much difference, so long as I get to Devon on the day I said I would. And it is hot, I admit, and I am still stiff."

A complacency of foreknowledge shone across his face. "Of

c

course," he cooed, "I knew you'd come back. It's all rot you were talking about having to go on. I knew it was all the time; we can get back for lunch at three. The worst of you men who've got tangled up in engagements . . ."

But by this time we were out and mounting the car, my knapsack going into the dickey with the beer and fish. "There in no time," said Aubrey resolutely; we whizzed off, skimmed round corners, mounted hills, skirted woods, and quite definitely were.

Sally was on the doorstep as soon as the car reached it, while the dogs yelped and bayed all round. "Mr. Aubrey said you'd be sure to be back, sir," she said, welcoming me in the most humiliating manner.

I very nearly went away, sulkily. In other words, I didn't.

This time it was fillet of sole, fried potatoes, and Double Gloucester; then coffee and brandy in the sitting-room. "I say," I said suddenly, "I really must get back into Winchester to-night. Do you mind if I go and lie down just for two hours; I'm still pretty tired."

"Certainly not," said Aubrey. "I'll wake you at six, and then we can go over and see George."

I mumbled: "Yes, splendid," though there was nobody in the world whom I wanted to see less than George, who, any-how, I reflected with bitterness, was only a fat facetious farmer, and I went upstairs, took off coat and shoes, put the eiderdown over me, and relapsed into a dream of racing horses with onions' heads and glaring lobsters' eyes on stalks, all heading for my hapless self.

When I awoke, the full daylight was still streaming through the windows. I rose, rinsed my face, and descended the stairs. Aubrey was deep in an armchair with a bottle of beer beside him, several books open on a table at his other hand, and an exercise book on his knee. His head was down and he was industriously writing. I felt like retiring, he looked so busy; but, hearing me, he flung everything down, exclaimed: "Only filling up the time with a few more notes on my *History of the Thoroughbred*," and added: "Well, if you're ready; supper isn't till eight and I hope you won't mind cold bacon again, and we might as well go and look them up at the 'Hare and Hounds.' "

I forgot, at any rate I did not mind forgetting, my resolution to proceed to Winchester that night. "But," I rejoined, "I thought you said we were going over to see George?"

"What, didn't I tell you?" he asked, surprised. "I thought I'd told you George has been off all day buying beasts near Basingstoke, and he won't be back till late."

There was no point in arguing, though such deceitfulness deserved rebuke. Once more the car was started and o'er moor and torrent, we reached the "Hare and Hounds." As we entered it loud voices, very late in the day, were discussing Larwood, Jardine, and the leg-theory; to my surprise, in the middle of the group, I saw the Gargantuan form of George, complete with his old school tie, vast expanse of yellow suit, and little eyes sunk deep in his pig-like face.

"Well, well, well!" gurgled George, extending a hand to each of us.

"Thought you were up around Basingstoke, George," said Aubrey.

"Beasts too dear, everything's too dear," said George. "I just came away. What'll you have?"

A confidential sermon on farming followed, from which I could only deduce that everything was at once too dear and too cheap; but we soon got back to cricket, and harmony with "dear old Maurice Read." Two hours flashed by in a general din, when Aubrey, who had been doing a circuit of the bar, came up cheerfully and said: "Look here, if you aren't hungry, I am." I was, and said so.

Shadows gathering, we drove back once more to the cold bacon. Something had changed Aubrey's mood. The silence in which he ate his meal was not the silence of appetite but the silence of worry. I felt uneasy; his brows were knitted, he ate, as it were, vindictively, and he looked as though he had something on his mind. When we settled down in the sitting-room he was uncharacteristically offhand when Sally brought in the coffee, saying: "Just put it down there and bring us in a bottle of claret and two glasses." "Good night, sir," said Sally, with unusual reserve, as she set the last things down. "Good night," he replied abstractedly, with his chin upon his hands and his eyes staring forwards and downwards. In the lamplight the sporting prints looked down on him compassionately; the old furniture was undisturbed.

I watched him with an unaccustomed scrutiny. That usually jolly and care-free face had become suddenly sombre and brooding.

He threw away a cigarette impatiently, and lit another. Then he turned to me and, speaking in a slow incisive voice, said: "Do you suppose that any of those chaps we saw to-day ever *think*?"

"I don't know," I replied. "I expect they do, when they're in trouble or in the silent watches of the night. I expect that everybody does who isn't a mere animal. You can't very well suffer without wondering why, or meditate alone without wondering where you came from."

"I've been worrying about it lately," said he, whom I had always supposed to concern himself only about cricket, beer, the crops, the garden, racing, and the utterly damnable eating-up of England by speculative builders, taxation, and the urban mind.

"About what?" I asked.

"About Truth," said he, "about what it's all about."

There flashed through my mind an old *Punch* dialogue: "What abart it?"—"Well, what abart what?"—"Well, what abart what you said abart me?" I checked myself, on grounds of tact and consideration, from repeating it, as flippancy, at the moment, would have been no balm for him. Nor did I remind him of the happiness of his diurnal pursuits; for he was aware of that, and trying, if not to escape from it, to relate it in some manner to the unhappiness of others, to the Universe, and to the ultimate mysteries of Death, Evil, and that wavering thing, the Categorical Imperative, which is (or was) a Prussian name for Duty and Conscience. Had it been earlier in the day and he in another mood I might have fetched his Bible (probably kept between Pitcher and Mrs. Earle) and read to him from the seventeenth chapter of the Gospel according to St. John. But I was his guest, I had to consort to his mood, I had (if possible) to cheer him up. I remembered that both St. Augustine and Cardinal Newman had had their doubts and guessed that St. Ignatius had had his, and I felt that, as his faith was waning with the night, the best thing I could do would be to sympathize with his scepticism and put the jolliest face possible upon that state of mind which was habitual to Pyrrho and the late Lord Balfour, and, probably, to the late Pontius Pilate. "Did I ever," I asked him, lighting a preparatory cigarette, pouring out another glass, and wishing there were a log to kick into a blazing fire, "tell you about that night I spent in Venice?"

"I suppose you mean you talked to a Catholic priest?" he replied, with the sullenness of the man who has been on the verge of Catholicism all his life.

"Nothing of the sort," I remarked, soothingly, "it's only that I had a dream and I don't know whether it was a dream."

"That sounds pretty good nonsense," he retorted, already resuming some semblance of his normal hearty, combative self.

"Not at all," I proceeded. "Did you ever hear of Chuang Tzu?" There was a long pause.

"No; I suppose he was a Chinese philosopher?"

"An easy guess, and quite correct. He lived some thousands of years ago. It is reported of him that when the Emperor (it was about the time when the earliest fine pots were made, which fetch so much in Boston) sent emissaries to ask him to be viceroy of a province, he replied that he was too busy watching a frog dive into a lily-pond. But there is also extant a story about him saying that he had dreamt he was a butterfly and that, for the rest of his life, he would not know whether he was a man dreaming that he was a butterfly or a butterfly dreaming that he was a man."

"Tight, I expect," said Aubrey surprisingly, with his usual gurgling laugh.

"Not at all," said I; "he knew a lot more about it than most of our modern philosophers, let alone all the business men to whom you object. But am I to go on with my story?"

"Carry on," said Aubrey, encouragingly, and emerging so far from his gloom as to fill his glass to the brim, "what was it?"

"You seem to have forgotten rather rapidly. But it doesn't matter: I will go on. I will tell you what happened to me in Venice."

"Leave out anything you don't want to tell," he interrupted, with some coarseness. I was tempted to reply rather hotly, but remembered that I was playing the game of distracting him, and merely remarked: "Now, are you going to listen?"

"Of course I am, old boy," he responded. "Carry on."

"Well," I went on mollified, "you can hear about my meeting with Truth, which I don't know whether it was a dream or not." Aubrey murmured something about grammar, but I went on, taking no notice.

"It had been," I said, adopting that artificial crooning voice which is usual with English people who think they are using poetical words, "a perfect evening after a long train journey. Dinner over the Lagoon, with the Maritime Customs House and Santa Maria della Salute, ornate but dignified, peacefully reposing across the end of the Grand Canal; an hour on the balcony, watching the pearl-grey of the far waters and sea-green of the near ones flushed red by the sunset and then dwindling into darkness, crossed by rippling plates of gold; then good night, early to bed, comfortable sheets, and a pink-shaded light on the little bedside table.

" 'I can't go to sleep yet,' I thought. 'Venice is much too lovely and I want to lie and think about it.' "

"Quite right," observed Aubrey, sipping his claret with his eyes closed, "but, I say, old boy, are you reading this?"

"No, I'm not! You can't expect me to talk about Venice in your Kempton Park slang, can you?"

"I didn't mean any offence. But there are rather a lot of adjectives, aren't there?"

"Venice is built of adjectives; am I to go on, or am I not?"

"Why, certainly, I am getting interested."

fall in love with illusions. If you want to know, I couldn't stand Plato at any price. He was simply a dreamer.' 'Well,' said I, 'at least you can't say that about Aristotle.' She shook her head on the pillow. 'Oh, for God's sake,' she muttered, 'don't talk to me about Aristotle. He was almost as bad as Bacon.'

" 'Surely both of them cared about Truth?' I queried. She flung herself up and cried: 'They didn't! They didn't! They didn't! They didn't care for me one little bit; they only cared about facts, for all their beastly brains.' She collapsed back on the pillow and sobbed and sobbed. 'All you do,' she lamented, 'is to pity all those silly old men and you don't think at all about what I've suffered at their hands. You men are all the same!' It's difficult enough, as every grown man knows, to console and comfort even a woman with whom one is intimately acquainted, but think of consoling a *déesse incomprise,* a refractory female whom one has never met before, and a border-line goddess at that. There was still the throbbing of a motor-boat on the lagoon; I looked at the still face and the recumbent form and I simply didn't know what to say. My problem was resolved by the lady. She peeped over her arm. "I wonder, dearie,' she said in a cajoling manner, 'that you didn't mention Schopenhauer.'

" 'Well,' I said, stumblingly, 'I don't much like him myself, and I think he must have been dyspeptic, but I do think he cared for you and that you ought to honour him.' She sprang up until she was almost out of the bed, her face contorted, her mouth working, her eyes as red as a ferret's. 'What!' she yelled, 'that horrible German beast? Why, he was a woman-hater!' Soothingly, her voice changed; in an enchantress's manner she said: 'Do *you* think I'm ugly?'

"I leant over her, as languorously she lay, and saw her face change from beauty to beauty; now that of a proud Egyptian queen, now that of a mysterious sibyl, now that of the soul of knowledge, now that of the soul of love, now that of a demure young virgin, innocent and wistful, early Florentine. In that one face, in that one minute, I saw all earthly and unearthly beauties.

" 'How,' thought I, 'could I ever have doubted this woman? Why should such a brute as myself have been vouchsafed such a vision?'

"She opened her eyes.

" 'Well,' said she, 'did you like it?'

"I couldn't answer.

" 'Anyhow,' she continued, 'do *you* think I'm ugly?'

" 'Goodness, goodness no!' I exclaimed, 'you're the loveliest thing that ever I saw in my life!'

" 'That's just where you're mistaken,' she remarked, very slowly and solemnly; and facing me square, squeezing up her eyes, projecting her lower jaw, and thrusting out her tongue between teeth that suddenly seemed to have grown like fangs: 'I can look like this, my boy, and don't you forget it! Oh no, it's no good thinking of hitting me. Even if you tried to, you couldn't hit *me!*'

" 'I wasn't even thinking of hitting you,' I grumbled.

" 'Don't lie!' she said. 'You can't take Truth in by lies, you know.'

" 'I wasn't lying!' I said.

" 'Don't lie again,' said she, looking as cunning as Satan. Then she turned her face into an image of The Soul's Awakening.

" 'I'm not lying!' I almost shouted; 'I'm only trying to understand you. You come in here and rob me of my sleep and I do my damnedest to find out what you want and I honestly think if you'd stay long enough and explain it I might be able to produce it, and it's horribly unfair of you to be evasive and elusive. I also think it's unfair of you to be so abusive about those unfortunate philosophers who only tried to do their best for you.'

"She leapt out of the bed.

" 'If anybody ever catches *me*,' she said disdainfully, "it will be a poet!'

"I moved to spring after her.

" 'Why shouldn't it be me?' I cried.

" 'Stay where you are!' she cried imperatively, stretching herself to her full naked height. I stayed where I was, as though shackled by iron.

" 'Sorry old thing!' she said, 'I've got to get back to my well!'

"Of course, she had the last word. Raising both arms and crooking both elbows she snapped the thumbs and fingers of both hands. There was a kind of whirling in the air, the lights swam, and when they settled down again she was gone.

"But there I was, in the bedroom of a Venetian hotel, with the water lapping against the sides of the moored gondolas and one solitary motor-boat humming far off in the distance. My hand automatically stretched out. It caught a paper; I lifted it up and gazed again at the effigy on the cover—that erect, virtuous, innocuous, sexless, lamp-bearing personality—so straight, so incapable of humour, beauty, wit or cruelty.

" 'You call yourself Truth,' I murmured, 'but little do you know what Truth really is!' "

*　　　*　　　*　　　*　　　*

It is all very well. But would you believe it? Just when I had finished telling Aubrey the story about my dream (if dream it was) I put out a hand in gesticulation, heard a dim crash, sprang up, listened for footsteps with a palpitating heart, switched on the bed-head light and saw the floor strewn with books, fruit, plate, knife and broken glass, and realized that I had never told Aubrey the story at all, that I had dreamt I had told him about my dream (if it was a dream), that I had gone to bed and that I had no dialogue with him at all! All the comments he had made; all my impatient retorts (not here recorded) about Anatole France's easy play with easy erudition, references to Tanagra statuettes and the philosophic fragments of Hypodermos of Syringa, were the mere smoke of slumber.

Happily it hadn't been a nightmare; I hadn't been falling over cliffs, fighting goblins who came together when hewn to pieces, or taking ten giant crocodiles on at once; so I re-arranged my pillows, turned out the light, curled up, and did not wake again until——

FOURTH DAY

Once more the sunshine was streaming through the window, and Aubrey was standing there in a florid silk red dressing-gown, carrying an equally florid blue one for me.

"Look here, Aubrey," I said, "I can't tell you how I've enjoyed my stay here. When I set out I thought I might see somebody in Kent and somebody in Wiltshire; but it was ever so much nicer seeing you."

"All right," said he, "but you must have breakfast before you go; what about a little cold bacon?"

Cold bacon it was, with the kind of chopped-up potatoes that I knew in Devonshire when I was a boy. Gorged, I remarked: "Old thing, it's extraordinary nice being here, but I simply must get on, for I have promised to be in Devonshire by a certain date."

"All right," he commented sulkily, "if you must go, you must go. I expect you will go farther and fare worse; but have it your own way."

He looked rather pathetic. It might be months before anybody who knew his primary language turned up again: he had his farm, his books, his Sally, and his neighbours, but all the winter might pass before he met another man who had heard of Baudelaire and Verlaine, let alone translating them at school. I was sorry for him (just as I was envious of him —he the Settled, I the Visitor, on and over the land we both loved) but I really had to remember that I was a householder with a programme, a father with a family, and an author with a contract.

So I set my upper lip and, to the epilogue of an orchestra of barking dogs, left him for the second time.

I went out of the village. I remembered, as I went, a poem which I had written when I was young, all about a man walking out of a village to the rainy hills, remembering the old gaffers and grannies, the blacksmith's shop, the old oak with the immemorial seat under it and the dogs asleep on the doorsteps in the middle of the day. That poem I never published, for I knew it was false; I preferred *Cranford* and Miss Mitford, and thought that the dogs were sensible to lie on the doorsteps in the idle of the day. But now I was forsaking all the comfort which was open to me to go off into the . . .

But of course I wasn't going "off into the . . ."

The world is getting gradually (I think it is the word) "taped." Young men wander, with cameras, through Chinese Turkestan and the Gran Chaco, and come back rather bored, to talk deprecatingly at cocktail parties about places concerning which Sir John Mandeville mightily lied, and of which all Othello knew was that there were people there who ate strange flesh, and others whose heads grew beneath their shoulders—whom we now knew not to have existed, whatever may have been the truth in Othello's time. All I was doing, never having heard the Abyssinian bird sing at that season of the year or been tempted to shoot an albatross, was to set out on a walk, well furnished with clothes and money, in the easiest climate and country in the world, and able to stop when I liked and where I liked.

Stop I did; on the top of a hill which surveyed fields (which looked good partridge-fields) and woods, which seemed to offer, provided the keepers and beaters got the birds up properly, good pheasant shooting. On that summit I rested, at about twelve-thirty, and took out of my pocket a hunk of bread and the last (if, indeed, it was the last) of Aubrey's cold bacon.

*   *   *   *   *

Seated alone, with a world of downland and sky around me, I found myself thinking of shooting. It was August, and already in Scotland the annual campaign had begun; men were standing in butts, all their senses keyed up to animal intensity, and for months now the whole island would ring with shots.

Suddenly remembering, I took from my pocket some tattered scraps of paper which I had intermittently carried about with me for years whenever there seemed a chance of leisure for concentration and completion, and which I had deliberately brought with me this time. On a sparkling November morning, starting early across the uplands for a day's pheasant shooting, I had felt exalted by the freshness of the earth, stopped the car, and written down lines whose meaning was perhaps more implicit than explicit:

> Could something stir in the lines
> Of the dark pines,
> And the pale ponds,
> And the fronds
> Of the bracken that browns
> On the downs:
> Could a word come down from the sky
> So blue, so pure, and so high.

And that night I sat alone, in front of a fire, in my study and meditated on the day and the poetry of it.

At luncheon in a hut over a tree-girt lake, we had been talking, as shooting men sometimes do talk, about the pros and cons of the pursuit, reassuring ourselves with the usual commonplaces about pheasants dying as comfortably as farm-yard fowls and the absurdity of meat-eating reformers attacking "blood sports." Somebody had said that, though he did occasionally like to let off his gun, he believed that the chief joy he found in a day's shooting was got between drives—all the wild life that was not shot and the lovely seclusion of preserves. Reflecting on all this alone I remembered many ecstatic moments I had had when shooting, twilights by duck-ponds, mornings on Scotch mountains, woodlands in mist, the glimpse of a wild deer in a Sussex thicket, the gorgeous feathers of a pheasant half-buried in deep snow, with drops of its blood looking like dry crimson dust on the soft whiteness. I was soon in a complex of memories and bewilderments, at one moment trying to recover a precise scene or train of thought and emotion, and at another wandering off in contemplation of the lives and deaths of birds and men; and then my mind harked back to the lines I had written in the morning and I thought they might be the opening of a poem on all the aspects of shooting and the vistas which it opens up, and in a heat of imagination I wrote, very rapidly, several disjointed passages which I thought might fit later into some shapely frame as yet undesigned.

There was a passage about watching a single high partridge coming over a hedge like a black star in the sky, and how, in its swift mounting approach it looks so intent and almost vindictive, like a bolt from the sling of an enemy, and how, the moment one goes to pick it up behind one, it seems so frail and harmless:

> Here, alas!
> Here it is on the grass.
> Here dead did it fall;
> And now lies so pathetic and small,
> Weary small head, soft feathers, a little bird,
> Such as long ago heard,
> Standing eager and trustful arow,
> (Heads up, being little) the happy miraculous words,
> The voice of the tender St. Francis, so patient and slow
> As he spoke to the birds:
> As he told the small birds that brothers, though simple,
>   they were,
> And the Lord had a thought for the fate of each bird of
>   the air;
> Though three farthings each worth
> It was known to the Lord as the greatest and proudest
>   on earth. . . .
> And he, 'neath the sky,
> So vasty and frore,
> Though a gown and a rope and a cowl and a halo he
>   wore
> Knew no more of the wherefore and why
> Than the stupidest bird of them all.

He told them also (I thought) that men, like birds, were timid and feared for their children and fluttered in senseless alarm—and I remembered a place where all these thoughts had flashed through my head, simultaneously (for one's thoughts have no regard for consistency and decency) with the old jingle about Frederick, Prince of Wales:

> Here lies Fred.
> Who was alive and is dead,
> There's no more to be said.

I went to pick the bird up; everything was as it was a few seconds before when it was alive and flying. There was an orchard of apple trees behind, a few brave clinging leaves and ruddy globes of fruit. Beyond the trees was a farm, and a child calling to another; up the hillside a plough was jingling; a car moaned by; but the bird was dead and nothing could bring it to life; and another bird, though it knew nothing of death or destiny, would be cold without a mate. And I consoled myself with common-sense reflections about the universality of death, and the mercifulness of this as compared with what birds have to face from Nature—frost, shortage of berries or water, the murderous nips of stoat and rat and fox—and I recalled how often that partridge, in unnecessary fright, had flown as fast before, because of passing cars or labourers, and how it had never known it was alive, or even for a moment that it was seeing the sun for the last time.

All that, seasons ago, I had written down. And I had tried to recover in verse the whole thrill of expectation in a ride curving through copses—alone in the world with a gun, the other guns hidden somewhere, young bare trees all around, twigs and fallen leaves on the dry grass, a pale sky and silence everywhere. There is a long wait, and then a rustle, and then silence again. There is a distant cry, a distant shot, and then silence again; and then there is a loud rattle of leaves in front and an old cock patters up, pauses, starts again, stares, then hurries on stirring leaves as he goes. Another rustle and a rabbit goes back; a jay crooks away; a grey squirrel meets its end; and then tap-tap, tap-tap, far right and far left and in front, comes the slow, relentless advance of the beaters, and rustling becomes multitudinous, and sly phantoms can be descried darting about in the depths of the wood, the cunninger,

PLAYER ONE

Douglas Coupland is the international bestselling author of *Generation X,* and eleven other novels, including *The Gum Thief, Hey Nostradamus!, All Families Are Psychotic,* and *Generation A.* His non-fiction books include *Marshall McLuhan, Polaroids from the Dead* and *Souvenir of Canada.* His books have been translated into thirty-five languages and published around the world. He is also a visual artist and sculptor, furniture designer and screenwriter. He lives in Vancouver, B.C.

ALSO BY DOUGLAS COUPLAND

Fiction
Generation X: Tales for an Accelerated Culture
Shampoo Planet
Life After God
Microserfs
Girlfriend in a Coma
Miss Wyoming
All Families Are Psychotic
Hey Nostradamus!
Eleanor Rigby
JPod
The Gum Thief
Generation A

Non-fiction
Polaroids from the Dead
City of Glass
Souvenir of Canada
Souvenir of Canada 2
Terry
Marshall McLuhan

Player**One**

What Is to Become of Us

Douglas Coupland

A Novel in **Five** Hours

WILLIAM HEINEMANN
LONDON

Published by William Heinemann 2010

2 4 6 8 10 9 7 5 3 1

Copyright © Douglas Coupland 2010

Douglas Coupland has asserted his right under the Copyright, Designs
and Patents Act, 1988, to be identified as the author of this work

First published in Canada in 2010 by House of Anansi Press Inc.

First published in Great Britain in 2010 by
William Heinemann
Random House, 20 Vauxhall Bridge Road,
London SW1V 2SA

www.rbooks.co.uk

Addresses for companies within The Random House Group Limited can
be found at: www.randomhouse.co.uk/offices.htm

The Random House Group Limited Reg. No. 954009

A CIP catalogue record for this book
is available from the British Library

ISBN 9780434021048 (Hardback)
ISBN 9780434021055 (Trade paperback)

The Random House Group Limited supports The Forest Stewardship
Council (FSC), the leading international forest certification organisation.
All our titles that are printed on Greenpeace approved FSC certified paper
carry the FSC logo. Our paper procurement policy can be found at:
www.rbooks.co.uk/environment

Pr ... and bound in Great Britain by Clays Ltd, St Ives Plc

CONTENTS

Hour One: Cue the Flaming Zeppelin 1

Hour Two: The Best of the Rest of Your Life 44

Hour Three: God's Little Dumpsters 89

Hour Four: Hello, My Name Is: Monster 133

Hour Five: The View from Inside Daffy Duck's Hole 172

Future Legend 215

With thanks to the following
for their care, thought, and research:

Thurman Allen
Debbie Audus
Steve Audus
Kathryn Bailey
Ala Bialas
Tim Bieniosek
Eve Brosseau
Jeremy Bye
Dylan Cantwell Smith
Jodi Crisp
Iam Crowley
Chelsea Damen
Monique Daviau
Elizabeth Davidson
Antonella DiFranco
Brian Draper
Elizabeth Dulley
Jaime Endick
Kevin Everest
John Fogde
Laura Foxworthy
Leanne Gebicki
Stephen Gray
K. C. Humphries
Anne Lawrence
Jessica Miller
Erik Mortensen
Kay Müller
Simon Nixon
Stephie Schlittenhardt
Erin Seiden
Goncalo Silva
Mary Silver
Mark Staples
Amanda Traphagan
Nikole Villanueva
Helena Vissing
Maria Wickens
Laura Winwood
Kate Wooley
Lara M. Zeises

"You can have information or you can have a life,
but you can't have both."
Doug's Law

HOUR ONE

Cue the Flaming Zeppelin

Karen

Karen likes crossword puzzles because they make time pass quickly. Karen makes quilts and donates them to charity because she savours the way quilting slows down time. Karen finds it strange that people who militantly remove time-expired dairy products from their refrigerator think nothing of abandoning a bottle of Kraft Catalina salad dressing on the fridge door's condiment shelf for years at a time. She herself is guilty of this crime. Karen remembers her ex-husband, back when things were good, scanning the fridge door and saying, "Jesus, Karen, this bottle of Thousand Islands remembers where it was during the Kennedy assassination."

Karen is almost forty and had thought she'd never find anyone again, but now she's flying to meet the man she hopes will become her lover. She is sitting in an aluminum fuselage zinging eastward, eight kilometres above Lake Superior. She's a little too warm, so she undoes two buttons at the top of her dress, hoping that if anyone sees her they won't take this as a sign that she is a slut. *Why*, she thinks, *should I care if strangers think I'm a slut? But I do.* Then she remembers that everyone has a camera these days, and any of those cameras might photograph her. Oh, those cameras! Those little bright blue windows she always sees from her back-row seat in Casey's school auditorium, a jiggling sapphire matrix of memories that will, in all likelihood, never be viewed, because people who tape music recitals tape pretty much everything else, and there's not enough time in life to review even a fraction of those recorded memories. Kitchen drawers filled with abandoned memory cards. Unsharpened pencils. Notepads from realtors. Dental retainers. The drawer is a time capsule. Karen thinks, *Everything we leave behind us as we move from room to room is a husk.*

There's a teenage boy across the aisle in the row ahead of Karen who has glanced her way a few times on this flight. Karen is flattered to think she might be considered hot — albeit a "hot mom" — but then she also knows that this horny kid probably has some kind of sin-detecting hand-held gadget lurking in his shirt pocket, lying in wait for Karen to undo more buttons or pick her nose or perform any other silly act that was formerly considered private, a silly act that will ultimately appear on a gag-photo website alongside JPEGs of baseball team portraits in which one member is actively vomiting, or on a movie site where teenagers, utterly unaware of the notion of cause and effect, jump from suburban rooftops onto trampolines, whereupon they die.

Modern technology be damned. Karen fiddles with her buttons. Her stomach grumbles. The right side of the plane is too bright, and she looks farther down the fuselage and she remembers an old TV movie in which all of the passengers in a 747 in mid-flight abruptly vanished, all save five who had been asleep and for that reason avoided vanishing. In the movie, the vanished passengers were represented by the clothing left behind in their seats. But Karen thinks it through a bit further. What does it mean for someone to vanish? Obviously your clothing would be left behind. But so would things like hair extensions, toupées, jewellery . . . the list would go on . . . dental veneers, crowns, pacemakers, metal pins left from bone surgeries . . . she thinks it through further . . . well, to be unpleasant, there would also be undigested food and — wait — now that she thinks about it, hair would be left behind, too, because TV cop shows have told her that hair has no DNA in it, save for the root follicle. And then, what about bones? Bones are made of calcium carbonate, which is just a chemical and not specific to Karen; bones would also have to be left behind — perhaps not the marrow, but . . . but wait, hadn't Karen once read that for every cell in the human body there are ten times as many outsider entities, such as bacteria, viruses, and fungi? So those, too, would be there along with the clothing. Yuck. Your body isn't even a body — it's an ecosystem.

Karen decides to push it even further . . . what about water? Water is just water, and not technically part of what defines Karen as Karen, so all the left-behind clothing and other muck on the 747's seats would be soaking wet. But then . . . but then what about all the cells in the body? How would they be classified: Karen or not-Karen? Egg cells would be left behind, as they're only half Karen, not pure Karen, only half of her DNA. Wait — here comes that word again, "DNA" . . . *DNA*. If Karen were to look deep into a sample cell, say a skin cell, it would become clear that only her DNA is actually *her*. The rest is just proteins and fats and enzymes and hemoglobin and . . .

. . . and then Karen has a vision of her soggy remains there in seat 26K. Rising from them would be a ghostly, gossamer-thin pantyhose-like creature made solely of Karen's DNA — the only thing about her she can honestly say *is* her. Pantyhose! Probably not even pantyhose, as all of the DNA extracted from her cells would be unconnected — all of her DNA would be a fine powder maybe the size of an orange. And then Karen is humbled, because she thinks of how little there is that makes her different from other people, a puff of dust. How corny and woo-woo and Eastern religion-y. And yet . . . and yet that's what is *her* — or is any of us. Dust. And somebody had better tell those fundamentalist Christians waiting for the Rapture to leave out some buckets and mops for those who are left behind.

Karen snaps out of her reverie. Her neighbour one seat over is watching a Discovery Channel documentary about larger things chasing and killing and eating smaller things. The Airbus 320 makes its laboured hushing sound. Karen wonders what Warren will be like. Karen met Warren on the Internet, and Warren is going to meet Karen in the cocktail lounge of the Toronto Airport Camelot Hotel. A cocktail lounge! How sleazy and how wonderful — and best of all, how low-commitment. If she and Warren click, it might be time to get a proverbial room upstairs. If the click doesn't happen, then it's right back to the airport and the next flight home. *Nature,* thinks Karen, *was very cruel yet very efficient when she invented clicking.* But what if there's no click: she likes Warren, but *only* likes him — liking without clicking? Well, it never works that way, does it? Off to the soul-crushing meat market, it is.

Karen turns to the window, and a speck of dirt on it makes her think, *Wouldn't it be great if stars turned black during the day — the sky covered with dots like pepper? A crescent moon is visible to the south. Imagine looking up at the moon and seeing it on fire!* For the first time in many moons, Karen feels as if her life is a real story, not just a string of events entered into a daybook — false linearity imposed on chaos as we humans try to make sense of our iffy situation here on earth. Karen thinks, *Our curse as humans is that we are trapped in time; our curse is that we are forced to interpret life as a sequence of events — a story — and when we can't figure out what our particular story is, we feel lost somehow.*

None of that for Karen, not today. The horny teen-ager across the aisle ever so discreetly holds up his iPhone and ever so discreetly takes Karen's photo, so Karen gives the camera the finger. She feels young again. And then she is struck by a sense of déjà vu; strange, because her current mission is unlike any she's undertaken before. And then the déjà vu passes and Karen is left wondering what life would be like if it were nothing *but* déjà vu — if life felt like a rerun all the time. She read something once about a person who had that condition, a lesion in the part of the brain that dictates one's sense of time. Is that all time is — our perception of how quickly it does or does not pass?

And then the plane begins its gentle slope into the airport. The captain says they'll be at the gate five minutes early. Karen experiences a rush of Christmas-morning feeling, the crazed, vibrating knowledge of wrapped toys beneath the tree, although the tree is actually an airport hotel cocktail lounge and the toy wrapped up in a box is Warren. *Now that's what I'd like*, Karen thinks. *The sensation of it being Christmas morning colouring every moment of my life.*

A huffy flight attendant tells Karen to raise her seat-back for landing. *Meddlesome cow.* Karen decides to torment the flight attendant by waiting until the absolute very last moment. She adjusts herself in her seat and wonders about Warren. What does she know about the man? Only what he has chosen to tell her about himself, as well as the qualities she attributes to him thanks to his prompt-without-being-*too*-prompt-hence-not-at-all-psycho response time to her emails, emails in which she has told him about her job (as a secretary for three psychiatrists, the trio of whom are thoroughly mad), her daughter (Casey, the moody fifteen-year-old violinist), her ex (Kevin, the bastard; at least he's planning to pay for Casey's college education), and . . . after those big strokes, what's to tell? We run out of things that make us individual very quickly; all of us have far more in common than we do not have in common. When Karen started working for doctors Marsh, Wellesley, and Yamato, she thought she would at least enjoy the voyeuristic thrill of transcribing the doctors' dictations after sessions — what fun to watch other people screw their lives up royally. And at first it was great, or rather, *Dear Warren, at first it was great — but then it suddenly started becoming not so great, because, in between the suicides and stalkings and breakdowns and drug overdoses, it emerged that there are only a few variations on the theme of madness, or rather, of being untypical: paranoia, autism, depression, anxiety, OCD, ADHD, and conditions that result from brain damage and growing old — well, you get the picture. All those Oliver Sacks books and online TED Conference speeches make craziness seem kooky and fun and compelling. Trust me, it's all about making people stick to their meds and not being driven crazy when the ADHDs fidget and tap their toes against the rack full of aging* InStyle *magazines in the waiting area.*

In his reply, Warren said he had once thought it would be interesting to be a priest, because you'd get to hear similar tales of peoples' dark sides in operation, except, when he thought it through, it might actually be dull as dirt, because there are only seven sins, not even eight, and once you've heard about nothing but seven sins over and over again, you must resort to doing Sudoku puzzles on the other side of the confessional, praying for someone, anyone, to invent a new sin and make things interesting again.

Sudoku? I love Sudoku, replied Karen. Warren liked it too. They were really connecting by then.

Warren: Karen is expecting a man around six feet tall, thinning hair but still with some shape to it, reasonably handsome — certainly handsome enough to be sexy, but not so handsome as to leave Karen in a state of perpetual unease around waitresses, secretaries, and post-grad students. *Wait — why am I fooling myself?* A man walks into a bookstore and looks up books on loneliness, and every woman in the store hits on him. A woman looks for books on loneliness, and the store clears out. It doesn't matter what sort of man you're discussing, the only attractive feature he need possess is a pulse. Oddly, being divorced and having a daughter makes it easier for Karen to meet new guys — online, at least. By one's early thirties, loss in all forms invariably makes its presence known. Children give Karen a common language to share with single fathers, one that childless people could never speak. And as long as one reined in the bitterness, divorce offers another commonality not shared by the perpetually single.

Karen knows she looks younger than forty. Perhaps thirty-six — or thirty-four with a drinking problem. In

Warren's photos — and there have been only two photos (should that have her alarm bells ringing?) — he seems to be a slightly sad man, and a bit cheap-looking, for some reason. It was hard to imagine him putting premium gas into his 2009 Ford Ranger, which was in the third JPEG he shipped, a photo with no human beings in it. *Please, God, don't let Warren be cheap. I'm too young to discuss coupons.*

Trudging off the plane, Karen enjoyed the status smorgasbord of jet deplaning: foil snack wrappers and Dan Brown paperbacks in coach class, copies of *The Economist* and *The Atlantic* abandoned in business class, and, of course, elderly and crippled passengers abandoned on the iceberg, deplaning only at the very end.

And then, sailing past the luggage carousel holding only carry-on baggage, Karen felt the not unpleasant tinge of superiority. *We envy those people who travel light, don't we?* At the carousel closest to the exit door stood a group of priests, and Karen got to thinking again about the seven deadly sins, and she wondered why there were Ten Commandments but only seven sins. One would think that, over the course of two thousand years, they might have harmonized that sort of thing. She walked past the pornographer-in-training teenage boy, travelling with his father and sister. He winked at Karen, and Karen laughed and walked out the electric doors. The rain had stopped, and sun leaked into the fringes of the taxi ranks. *What a beautiful day! Yessirree, nothing could possibly go wrong on a beautiful day like today.*

Cue the flaming Zeppelin.

Karen's good-mood bubble was quickly popped when she got into a taxi and informed her driver that she wanted to go to the nearby Camelot Hotel. The driver was livid that she was not a big, juicy downtown fare. His friend passing by in another cab rolled down his window, and Karen knew that her good name was being trashed in some language in which all the words sounded like *boobaloo*. Six minutes later the cab dropped her off in front of the Camelot Airport cocktail lounge building, a defeated concrete satellite of the main hotel that resembled the third-best restaurant in the fourth-largest city in Bulgaria. The cabbie zoomed away as Karen was slamming the door. She decided to find the incident funny rather than annoying. Sometimes life leaves you no other choice, and besides, her present beneath the tree was waiting to be opened.

Rick

Rick has stopped listening to the voice inside his head. Thirty-seven years of listening to his inner voice landed him nothing but bankruptcy, loneliness, and a rosacea that colours his face with a perpetual whisky sunburn — or rather, whisky gave him the permanent whisky sunburn; it was his interior voice that suggested he drink the whisky: *Come on, Rick, you deserve it, man! You planted a fifty-foot-long yellow cedar hedge this afternoon!* But Rick isn't listening to that voice any longer. Now he listens to other people as he tends the bar, and people tell Rick everything: abortion holidays to Bermuda, daydreams of gender reassignment surgery, harsh scolding mothers, and fears about North Korean missiles. People tell Rick the truth about themselves because Rick works in an airport hotel lounge bar and is hence transient and disposable within his guests' universes. Most bartenders only get to hear regulars lie about their lives, but airport bars have no regulars — just drinkers without roots and with temporarily absent inhibitions. Rick sees himself as a golden Labrador that people stop on the street so they can free-associate their inner thinking: *Oh, aren't you just the loveliest little dog, you are! Tell you what, I got caught jacking off in the supply room, and that's why I got fired, not like I told my wife, that I was blackballed for whistle-blowing. Hey, any more of these nuts — maybe a bowl with some actual cashew nuts in it, not just fragments?*

Rick wishes that one day someone would come in and confess that he was the one who stole Rick's pickup with all of his gardening equipment in it, but he knows that's probably not going to happen and that, truth be told, he drank away his landscaping career as well as his savings and his visitation rights, and all he has to show for it is a permanent sunburn and a dark aura that scares away the women who might like him, even though, over the decade-long span of his decline, he has become a listener and women *like* listeners. Or they're supposed to.

Oh well. Rick has serenity now. Kind of. Yet by and large he wonders why it is that we're trapped inside our bodies for seventy-odd years and never once in all that time can we just, say, park our bodies in a cave for even a five-minute break and float free from the bonds of earth.

At least music allows you to escape your body — in its own way. Rick feels nostalgic for the lounge's pianist, Lenny, who was fired two weeks earlier for consistently making up the lyrics to songs as he played. Rick was used to it, but patrons hated it. When the night manager called Lenny to the bar area for his third and final warning, Lenny said, "The lyrics of a song are important only to a point. You probably don't even remember the words to your favourite song, and that's why you like it — because you like the words your brain made up to fill in the gaps. A good song forces you to invent your own lyrics."

"Lenny, it's the goddam Beatles singing goddam 'Yesterday.' You do not invent lyrics for one of the most famous songs in history."

"I bring *myself* into the song. I am an artist. People listening to songs are like people reading novels: for a few minutes, for a few hours, someone else gets to come in and hijack that part of your brain that's always thinking. A good book or song kidnaps your interior voice and does all the driving. With the artist in charge, you're free for a little while to leave your body and be someone else."

Poor Lenny, now jobless, but Rick remembers what Lenny said about leaving your body for a little while — Rick remembers liking that bit — and in memory of Lenny he cranks the Miles Davis CD now playing — music without lyrics. Instead of inventing words to the music, your body invents emotions for the music.

Rick sees a rogue glass shard from a bottle of southern-hemisphere Chardonnay he dropped the night before. As he bends to pick it up, he remembers Tyler's seventh birthday, sitting with his son in a bedroom fort made of whisky boxes and blankets and sofa cushions, and he remembers shining a flashlight through his fingers and through Tyler's, trying to convince his son that people are made of blood. He misses the good days and fondly remembers the rare mornings that were magically free of hangovers and when his head felt like a house in late spring with all the doors and windows wide open. And he wishes he hadn't knocked over the twenty-ounce Aladdin souvenir plastic drinking cup full of $8.99 Chardonnay that night he was allowed to babysit Tyler while his ex-wife, Pam, was at her sister's stagette party. Half a squeeze bottle of organic dish soap and six towels washed and dried twice, and she's barely in the door, sniffing and saying, "That's it, Failure Face. You've had your chance. Out. Now."

Mercifully, one thing people rarely tell Rick about is their dreams — both actual dreams and the dreams they have for the rest of their lives. We're always hearing about "following your dream," but what if your dream is boring? Most people's dreams are boring. What if you had a dream to sell roadside corn — if you went and sold it, would that mean you were living your dream? Would people perceive you as a failure anyway? And how long would you be happy doing it? Probably not long, but by then it would be too late to start something else. You'd be screwed. Rick now believes that there is much to be said for having a small, manageable dream. Rick has a small, manageable dream, except nobody knows about it but him. He is going to spend the $8,500 he's cobbled together since he sobered up, and he's going to spend it all on the Leslie Freemont Power Dynamics Seminar System. Leslie Freemont's compelling television ads promise Power! Control! Money! Friends! Love! . . . none of which Rick currently possesses.

Mister, you can't just leave the world. You can't just kill yourself. That's not an option. So you have to change your life. You're worried. You're worried that you're never going to change. You're worried that we might not even be able to change. Aren't you!

I am!

Mister, I am here to speak to you about transforming your life and yourself. Making choices and changing who you are. *You're going to become different. Your behaviour will be changing. Your thinking is going to change. And people will watch these changes in you and they'll come to experience the world in your new manner. You will become a teacher yourself. Are you ready to change, to join, to become part of What's Next?*

Yes!

Is the price of reinvention worth the effort?

Yes!

Reinvention costs $8,500, and as Rick wipes the rims on a set of Pilsner glasses, he remembers being at Tyler's peewee soccer game and making the mistake of confiding his enthusiasm for Leslie Freemont to Pam. She said, "Jesus, Rick, only losers make decisions when things are bad. The time to rejig your life is when things seem smooth."

That's Pam, and that's her way of looking at the world. But Leslie Freemont believes there is nothing human beings can do that cannot be considered human or magnificent: passion, crime, betrayal, loyalty. Leslie Freemont asks his followers to think of a single act a human being could commit that would be considered nonhuman. It's impossible; as soon as a human performs any act, that act becomes human. Leslie Freemont says we know what dogs do: they bark and they form packs and they circle their beds before they lie down to sleep. Leslie Freemont says we know what cats do: they rub

your shins when they want tuna and they can be hypnotized by dangling yarn. But humans? Humans are special because humans do *all* things. There is no emotion
possessed by any other creature on earth that is not
also experienced by humans. Leslie Freemont says that
makes us divine, and Leslie Freemont can help Rick tap
into all of that.

Rick is giddy because Leslie Freemont is soon going
to be in this very hotel; he'll be entering this very cocktail lounge. Leslie is on his way here because Rick's basement neighbour, Rain Man, saw that Leslie was in town
doing seminars and tracked down Freemont HQ on the
Internet and convinced Leslie to come in on his way to
the airport — a mission to meet a Common Man for a
photo op.

Rick would have tracked down Leslie himself, except
that his PC died ages ago and is now out on his balcony,
collecting birdshit and grit. Its dead keyboard covers
his canister of protein powder on the kitchen counter,
the original plastic lid having long ago been sacrificed
as a Frisbee for Rain Man's Rottweiler, whose fangs
mangled it into chewy red lace, making Rick think, *Man,
Rick, at what point did your luck turn? At what point did
you switch from being a story to being a cautionary tale?
People's lives shouldn't have a moral attached to them —
they should be stories without morals, told purely for joy.*

But the Leslie Freemont Power Dynamics Seminar
System can strip Rick's life of pathos, and Leslie will be
arriving at any moment. Rick knows this because Leslie's

press woman, Tara, phoned to say that Leslie wants to personally shake Rick's hand and have a photo taken with him as Rick hands over his $8,500 in cash. Rick feels almost the way he used to halfway through his third drink, his favourite moment, the way he wishes all moments in life could feel: heightened with the sense that anything could happen at any moment — that being alive is important, because just when you least expect it, you might receive exactly what you least expect.

———

Rick said to the woman, "Where are we — trapped inside a Bob Hope movie?"

The woman at the bar, a nice little brunette, looked at Rick. "Very funny. Is it so wrong for a girl to order a Singapore sling?"

"I'm going to have to look it up in my mixology book back here."

"Don't bother. I'll google it on my thingy. Wait a second . . . there . . . you'll need one ounce of gin, a half-ounce of cherry brandy, four ounces of pineapple juice, the juice of half a lime, a quarter-ounce of Cointreau, a quarter-ounce of Benedictine, a third of an ounce of grenadine syrup, and a dash of Angostura."

Rick looked at the woman. "You're here on an Internet hookup, aren't you?"

His customer's head did a chicken bob. "Honey, you are *good*. How did you *know* that?"

"I can always tell. Where're you from?"

"Winnipeg, and you didn't answer my question."

"Okay, you asked, so I'll answer. I can tell you're here for an Internet hookup because you're sitting with good posture on a bar stool but you're not a hooker. Hookups never sit in booths, because it makes them look sad or desperate, but a bar stool — especially when you have good legs like yours, I might add — says to someone new, 'Hey, let's get it on.' Also, you've got a tiny carry-on bag, which means you're most likely not staying at this hotel or any hotel."

The woman asked, "In general, how do these hookups usually go?"

"It's always hot or cold. No middle ground. You either both click and you're out of here and upstairs pronto, or there's an awkward forty-five-minute drink of doom followed by several lonely drinks for the person who stays behind while the other one flies home."

"I hope there are no drinks of doom for me."

Rick scanned the room with its mismatched grey fabrics and furniture. His eyes rested on the astonishingly beautiful young woman — nineteen? — who'd been using the world's most cobbled-together Internet booth across the lounge. The computer carrel comprised a power bar covered in duct tape attached to a brick-like North Korean monitor and hard drive, all shaded by a dusty plastic ficus tree. The beautiful girl's computer made a casino slot machine's *ching-ching-ching* noise. It stopped as soon as it had started. Rick called out, "Another ginger ale?" The girl looked emotionlessly at Rick. "No. I am properly hydrated."

The woman raised her eyebrow at Rick. *"No. I am properly hydrated'?"*

"She's a weird one, Miss Ginger Ale is. Cold fish, but not a cold fish. Like something's missing."

"She spurned your advances?"

"She's too young for me, thank you. And she's not the advances type."

"Too pure for this world?"

"Please. It's a challenge to the laws of physics that someone that beautiful is even in this lounge."

"Thanks for making me feel great."

"You know what I mean."

She nodded. She and Rick looked at the only other person in the bar — a trainwreck of some sort who probably used to play hockey on weekends but now he's going fleshy, maybe halfway between William Hurt and Gérard Depardieu. He sure looked like he could use a nap.

Rick felt a bond of alertness between him and the woman, of having something to look forward to. Rick looked at his watch.

The woman said, "It seems to me you're expecting someone, too."

"As a matter of fact, yes, I am."

"Really? Who?"

"You'll see."

"I'll *see*? What — is it George Clooney, maybe? Or perhaps Reese Witherspoon with a posse of Muppets?"

"Someone you'll recognize."

The woman was intrigued. "You're serious."

"I am."

"Huh. When is our celebrity supposed to arrive?"

"Any time now. What about your Mister Hookup?"

"Any time now."

Rick, disinhibited by the imminence of Leslie Freemont, threw out a conversation starter: "You know, I've been thinking about time a lot today."

"Have you?"

"I have. Wouldn't it be kind of cool," he said, "if time stopped right now?"

"How do you mean, if time stopped?"

"Like this. I was in England once, taking my father to see my grandmother, who was dying of emphysema. So, one morning we were on a train headed from London to wherever, when suddenly the train stopped with our car halfway inside a tunnel, and then the conductor turned off the train and an announcement came on that we were to observe two minutes of silence, and everyone went still and looked at their laps, even the soccer hooligans and their cellphones — and it was like the universe had suddenly turned itself off and the world was almost holy, like life was suddenly religious, but *good* religious, and suddenly everyone became the best version of themselves."

The woman looked at Rick. "I'm Karen."

"Rick."

They shook hands as the trainwrecky guy down the bar stared, breaking the moment by asking for a neat Scotch.

Luke

Luke is nursing a Scotch and wondering why it is that having money makes people feel so good — medically, scientifically, clinically *good*. What chemicals does it release? What neurons does it block? And just why is it an absolute given that having money — some money, *any* money — always feels better than having no money? There was a quote at the bottom of the snarky email sent to him yesterday by the Bake Sale Committee, one of those automatically attached quotes from some Internet program, and, as it was written by Oscar. Wilde, probably went unread by the dutiful committee member. It said, "The thing about being poor is that it takes up all of your time." So true.

But Luke is a pastor at a church locally known as "The Freeway Exit Church" more than by its proper name, The Church of New Faith, and so he has his own spin on money. He knows that what makes human beings different from everything else on the planet — or possibly in the universe, for that matter — is that they have the ability to experience the passing of time and they have the free will to make the most of that time. Dolphins and ravens and Labrador dogs come close, but they have no future tense in their minds. They understand cause and effect, but they can't sequence forward. It's why dogs in dog shows have to be led from task to task, because they're unable to sequence. They live in a perpetual present, something humans can never do, try as they may. And the reason Luke is thinking about time and free will is because he believes that money is the closest human beings have ever come to crystallizing time and free will into a compact physical form. Cash. Cash is a *time crystal*. Cash allows you to multiply your will, and it allows you to speed up time. Cash is what defines us as a species. Nothing else in the universe has *money*.

Luke — shaggy haired, a bit pudgy, and slightly rumpled, in designer garments nabbed from the church's flea market the previous April — currently has lots of money, because just this morning he looted the church bank account. It wasn't something he set out to do when he woke up, but now, with a few drinks in him, he understands that it was a long time coming, and that it took a specific incident to trigger the theft. The incident transpired like this: Late yesterday afternoon, Luke met with the women from the Bake Sale Committee to discuss the upcoming sale. Luke doesn't normally like chairing these meetings and has long-time volunteer Mrs. McGinness do it, but Mrs. McGinness is still in Arizona, helping her meth-whore daughter through her latest divorce. So Luke was sitting there, ready to chair the meeting, and eight women were supposed to be there, but only seven showed up. Luke asked, "Where's Cynthia?" and the ladies at the table mumbled whatever, so Luke said, "Isn't it funny that the Rapture finally happens and the only person to be taken away is Cynthia?"

Talk about the dog farting. Seven sour faces gave Luke the permission he didn't know he needed or was looking for to empty the church's renovation fund and vanish. It was such a clear, lucid moment, like the fugue he feels just before the onset of one of his small seizures. If the bank had still been open, he would have gone right then. And if he had any doubt about his new criminal calling, it was squelched by Sharon Truscott's clipped little email a few hours later saying that the ladies didn't appreciate having their piety mocked.

And now Luke is in a cocktail lounge that's meatlocker cold and smells of cleaning products in a city he's never visited before, with twenty grand in his jacket pockets, bundles of cash that sit like stones in a suicide's garment, weights meant to take one faster and more thoroughly to the bottom of the river — or perhaps they're more like helium balloons that will only take him higher and higher.

Or perhaps they will make him drunker.

Luke orders another Scotch from the bartender, who looks like one of those guys with multiple DUIs and revoked driving licences, and who's busy chatting up a middle-aged, barflyish, Sharon-like woman. He has just overheard them introducing themselves as Rick and Karen. Karen is obviously there to hook up with someone she's met on the Internet. Luke can't believe how many people meet on the Internet these days. It came out of nowhere and now it's the cause of over half the problems his flock comes to him with: online gambling debt, get-rich-quick schemes, porn addiction, parents freaked out about the sites their kids visit, shopaholism.

He can't even call the things people do on the Internet *sins*, because it's all so dull, really, just people sitting in front of screens, and what's *that*? Who cares? Ministering to souls was way more interesting when people actually interacted in real life. He hasn't had a shoplifter or an affair within his flock in years. Now *that's* interesting — oh so human — but Internet sinning? Nope. Goddam Internet. And his computer's spell-check always forces him to capitalize the word "Internet." Come on: World War Two *earned* its capitalization. The Internet just sucks human beings away from reality.

Luke wonders what Shakespeare had to say about money. Something clever, no doubt. Goddam Shakespeare. Luke used to pepper his sermons with lofty Shakespearean quotes because he thought it made him look smarter than he really was, and it also made his flock feel smarter because it validated any years they'd spent in college or university. But lately the younger flock members have let it be known to Luke that his quotes are kind of boring and mechanical and remind them of those automatic quotes by Nietzsche or Kafka that web bots insert at the bottom of emails that somehow, in some almost impossible to connect way, funnel truckloads of cash into the ever-expanding Eastern European pornography industry. And a Scotch with ice certainly helps lubricate Luke's belief that intelligence has been democratized and flattened. Luke feels both behind and in front of the curve.

The curve. What the hell is "the curve"?

Luke hates the twenty-first century.

Luke is a thief.

Luke remembers once believing in what he believed in: that one day he would no longer have to live inside linear time; the concept of infinity would cease to be frightening. All secrets would be revealed. Automobile ignitions would refuse to turn over; parking lots would melt like chocolate; water tables would vanish; and the planet would begin to cave in on itself. There would be great destruction; structures such as skyscrapers and multinational corporations would crumble. His dream life and his real life would fuse together. There would be loud music. Before he began to turn immaterial, his body would turn itself inside out and fall to the ground and cook like steak on a cheap hibachi, and he would be released and he would be judged and he would be found pure.

But his congregation talks about the afterlife as if it were Fort Lauderdale.

Whatever. What matters now is that Luke is practically vibrating with freedom.

And he has decided that, although he is a failure, failure is authentic, and because it's authentic, it's real and genuine, and because of that, it's a pure state of being, unlike the now-hopefully-dead fakey-fakey Luke — and feeling authentic feels great! *Heck, maybe I'm an outlaw now — I* am *an outlaw now!*

And now Luke has twenty grand in his pockets, and he's watching a little red-headed dude come into the bar and put his hand on Karen's thigh. She doesn't look too happy to meet him. Screw it. They'll both just keep looking until they each settle for someone equal to themselves on the food chain. That's the way Charles Darwin works.

Luke's conscience suddenly rattles him. By force of habit, he talks to a God he once believed in, but this time with a small twist: *Lord, I know that faith is not the natural condition of the human heart, but why did You make it so hard to have faith? And now it's too late, because I don't believe in You anymore. Why did I never discuss my doubts with any human beings? My elders could have set me on the righteous path. But maybe in the end it's best to keep one's doubts private. Saying them aloud cheapens them — makes them a bunch of words just like everybody else's bunch of words. If I'm going to fall, I'll do it on my own terms.*

Ironically, being honest with himself about his crime is making Luke feel genuinely spiritual as he looks at the cool Hitchcock blonde at the pathetic "business centre" across the room. He wonders if she's noticed him. What would she think of his crime? Luke thinks she'd look at his shoes in particular, and those shoes would speak to her, and what they would say is "Payless," and she'd write him off, so screw her; the moment he gets into town, he's buying a pair of ultra-executive shoes in a swanky store, and he'll never feel ashamed of his grim footwear ever again.

What's that? She just looked at him — and she's smiling? Hot *diggity*!

Hot diggity and yet: *crippling fear.* Lovely on the outside, most likely monstrous on the inside — if his former
flock is any litmus. She's most likely addicted to video
games and online shopping, bankrupting her parents in
an orgy of oyster merino and lichen alpaca. Fancy a bit of
chit-chat? Doubtful. She'd most likely text him, even if
they were riding together in a crashing car — and she'd be
fluent in seventeen software programs and fully versed in
the ability to conceal hourly visits to gruesome military
photo streams. She probably wouldn't remember 9/11
or the Y2K virus, and she'll never bother to learn a new
language because a machine will translate the world for
her in 0.034 seconds. But most of all, this cool Hitchcock
blonde is a living, breathing, luscious, and terrifying ter-
minal punctuation mark on Luke's existence, a punctuation mark along the lines of *This is the New Normal, Luke,
and guess what — it's left you in the weeds, and you, pastor,
reverend, good sir, have outlived your cultural purpose and
you, father, forgive me, are a chunk of cultural scrap metal,
not even recyclable at that. Go huddle together for security
with those other doddering, outmoded walking heaps there
at the bar with you. Compare your turkey-wattle chins and
Play-Doh waistlines and grow misty-eyed discussing the
collapse of Communism and the final episode of* Friends.

———

Having figured all of this out, Luke remained unsure
what to do. Cultural irrelevance be damned, he hadn't

had a date in over a year. A date: he cursed himself for his self-censorship; Luke hadn't *gotten laid* in years.

He smiled back at the blonde, who actually seemed a bit awkward. With his head, he motioned her over to the bar. She froze, and Luke thought, *Oh crap, too forward*. But then she stood up and walked over to Luke with a strangely mechanical gait. He wondered if she was a model, and if that was how models were walking these days. *She's so beautiful*, Luke thought. *Cartoon beautiful. She's a Barbie doll.*

She approached Luke, touched the stool beside him, and said, "I am going to sit here."

"Please do."

She sat on the stool, but her body language made it seem as if she'd never sat on a bar stool before and it had a learning curve, like learning how to ice skate or juggle. She stabilized and stared at the bottles against the bar's mirrored wall. Luke looked at her, and she seemed unconcerned about being stared at. He said, "A guy walks into a bar, and the bartender looks at him and says, 'Hey, what is this — a joke?'"

If Luke wanted a reaction, he didn't get it. "My name is Luke."

There was a pause. "My name is . . ." There was another pause. ". . . Rachel."

"Nice to meet you, Rachel."

"Yes."

Luke felt way out of his league, and awkward as all get-out. He needed to order more drinks, and maybe

some snacks, but what do you feed a woman like this —
hamburgers made of panther meat? Peacock livers on
Ritz crackers? Do beautiful women even eat food? "Can
I order you a drink?"

"Oh. Yes. A ginger ale, please."

"Great. Bartender?" Luke called for Rick's attention
but got only part of it, as Rick was watching the loving
Internet couple interact.

"What can I get you?"

"A ginger ale for Rachel here, and a Glenfiddich with
ice for me."

"Right away."

Luke reached into his jacket pocket for one of the
wads of cash and threw a fifty-dollar bill on the bar, and
suddenly he was carried away back in time — back to
when he still thought of himself as a good person; back
to when every moment made him feel as if he was getting
away with something; back to when he didn't need to loot
twenty thousand dollars from the church bank account to
land himself that feeling; back to when every moment
felt like a drink with a beautiful woman at a bar; back to
when he felt that his prayers still counted, still made a
difference, when praying sent a beam out into the heavens as powerful as a sunbeam breaking through clouds at
the end of a prairie day, like a light beamed from a side-
walk outside the Kodak Theater at the Academy Awards.
Luke didn't feel lost, but he didn't feel found, either.

On the mute TV above the bar, there was an ad for
something colourful, useless, and no doubt destined to

clog the planet's overtaxed landfills with more crap, and for some reason, a computer-animated Rudolph the Red-Nosed Reindeer was endorsing the product. Luke said, "Rudolph the Red-Nosed Reindeer in July? We need Christmas in July like a hole in the head."

The beautiful Rachel said, "You mean Rudolph the *Useful* Reindeer."

"Huh?"

"It's a fact, Luke. If Rudolph hadn't been able to help the other reindeer, they'd have left him to be eaten by wolves. I think the other reindeer would have laughed while the fangs punctured his hide. Rudolph was an outcast who became an incast only because of his utility. That's not a judgement. It's a statement of fact."

Luke looked at Rachel. He had a shivering sensation that he was speaking with someone not even human, temporarily given human form. Was he simply being insecure about her beauty or was she genuinely alien? Or perhaps she was the desired end product of an entire century's eugenic efforts at physical perfection, and with that perfection now having been achieved, humanity was now left free to pursue other avenues of perfection. He said, "I take it you're not a big fan of Christmas?"

"I have no orthodox beliefs. I have no pictures of an afterworld for myself. In the past, I have tried to convince myself that there is life after death, but I have found myself largely unable to do this."

Alcohol loosens tongues, and Luke knew he was in the presence of an unusual mind. He asked Rachel, "Do you believe in sin?" As he asked this, he was wondering if she considered him hot. At the same time, he was wondering if he had a chance with her. At the same time, his subconscious was churning through a list of random images: the church basement on a Tuesday morning, lit by a cold sun through the south window and quiet as abandoned Chernobyl; fragments of old *Battlestar Galactica* episodes beaming from his TV while he watched from the kitchen, eating Campbell's soup straight from the can; a trio of sparrows outside his bedroom window, fighting over who got control of the ledge.

Rachel said, "I believe only in human behaviour. And I think that if your brain forces you to believe in sin, then you at least ought to calibrate sinning. Religions seem to have no Richter scale of what's worse than something else. If you do one thing wrong, no matter how small, you're cast away for eternity. I also find it interesting that no religion has any dimension of ecological responsibility." Rachel paused. "Luke, I get the impression that you once believed in religion but you no longer do. Am I correct in thinking this?"

Part of Luke was wondering about Rachel's speech patterns; hers was neither an indoor voice nor an outdoor voice — something like robotized phone menus for United Airlines: *The estimated waiting time for the next available member of the United Airline's quality assurance team is ... seventy-five minutes.* The rest of Luke was thinking about all the dark secrets he knew about his former congregation — might as well start thinking about them in the past tense now — and he thought about his family members and all the crap they put everyone else through. And he thought about his friends and their families and their ongoing family scandals. And he acknowledged that every human on earth is a bubbling cauldron of dirt and filth. Then Luke became slightly spaced out and looked once more at the TV monitor above the bar: BUS CRASH INJURES THREE. HYDRO RATES TO INCREASE 1.5 PER-CENT. OPEC MEETING GENERATES CONFLICT. *All the crap and evil and meanness in the world — every single person on the planet! — and the best the news can come up with is BUS CRASH INJURES THREE?*

Luke looked at Rachel. "Yup. I no longer believe in God."

"Oh. Okay. Why is that?"

"Because one morning I saw a sparrow yawn."

"Yawning as in waking-up yawning?"

"Yes."

Rachel

Rachel is sitting at a bad computer in an airport hotel cocktail lounge with red plasticky walls and is contemplating leaving but decides to stay because she is on a mission, a mission that began because last winter, outside the kitchen, she heard her father say to her mother, "God, what a waste of a human life."

"Ray, don't talk like that. We need to find a way to get her to meet people. Maybe some men her age."

"And then what — she's going to get married and raise a happy family?"

"Ray, why are you even bringing this up?"

"I'm bringing this up because we never bring it up. No grandkids. No son-in-law. No nothing, just a robot forever, working in the garage eighteen hours a day . . . She has no sense of humour. Medically, clinically, scientifically, no sense of humour. And for that matter, no sense of irony or empathy or affection or —"

"I'm glad we're talking about this. You think marriage is an option for her? You think her having a child would make everything better?"

"Frankly, I do. Never been kissed. Never will be kissed. Christ, how sad."

"Stop!"

As a result of overhearing her father's sentiments, Rachel has determined that her life's mission is to bear children and thus prove to the world her value as a human being. She sees childbirth as a profoundly human act, and she would like to try to be human. She's unsure why she was not allowed to be human, but she now sees a chance to make her move.

Growing up, she tried to make herself human. She researched what makes humans different from all other creatures, and all she learned was that only humans create art and music — elephants paint with brushes, but that somehow doesn't count. And only humans tell jokes, only humans cook, only humans have an incest taboo, and only humans have ritual burials. Rachel dislikes and doesn't understand music, because all it is is sounds; she doesn't understand art, because all it is is scribbles and dribbles that don't mesh with photographic reality; and she doesn't understand humour or the notion of funniness — she only observes confusing braying-type sounds made by people after they hear something called "funny" (and usually after they've been drinking alcohol). However, from breeding white laboratory mice in the garage, she knows that an incest taboo is genetically useful, so she's all for a taboo. And burial rituals strike her as smart, because they allow people to turn back into soil and be useful.

Identifying the unique threads of the human condition is not something Rachel approaches lightly, and she is not deceived into thinking that high technology is an activity that makes humans different: complex human activities such as enriching uranium, for example, are, by extension, elaborate means of generating heat and of fighting — and there's nothing special to humans about that. Smashing atoms into quarks and leptons is high-tech, but if you think about it, it's merely a way of creating incredibly tiny, expensive building bricks, and bricks make houses and birds make nests, so what's special about that? Rachel once thought that attempts to contact alien species might constitute unique human behaviour, but it's really no different than a wolf cub standing in the shrubs around a human fire, hoping to be asked to come closer and join a tribe of a different species. But music, art, and humour? Rachel has to take it on faith that these human qualities exist.

Rachel has never fit into the world. She remembers as a child being handed large wooden numbers covered in sandpaper to help her learn numbers and mathematics. Other children weren't given tactile sandpaper number blocks, but she was, and she knows that she has always been a barely tolerated sore point among her neuro-typical classmates. Rachel also remembers many times starving herself for days because the food that arrived at the table was the wrong temperature or colour, or was placed on the plate incorrectly: it just wasn't *right*. And she remembers discovering single-player video games and for the first time in her life seeing a two-dimensional, non-judgemental, crisply defined realm in which she could be free from off-temperature food and sick colour schemes and bullies. Entering her screen's portal into that other realm is where her avatar, Player One, can fully come to life. Unlike Rachel, Player One has a complete overview both of the world and of time.

Player One's life is more like a painting than it is a story. Player One can see everything with a glance and can change tenses at will. Player One has ultimate freedom; the ultimate software on the ultimate hardware. That realm is also the one place where Player One feels, for lack of a better word, normal.

Rachel also knows she is something called "beautiful," but she has no idea what that is. Until she was seven, she was unable to look into a mirror without screaming. If you showed her a collection of photos of different people with one of herself in the group, she'd be hard pressed to find herself in the lot. But she knows that because she has this thing called "beauty," people treat her differently than they would if she did not possess it. According to her father, having beauty makes her existence tragic — whatever "tragic" means. She can't figure that out, either. It means that something good happened but was then wrecked. It means a waste of a human being.

But Rachel is going to prove that she is not a waste. For example, she has proven that she can dress herself stylishly, just like a regular human woman. She read in a magazine that all women should have a little black dress and that all women love Chanel clothing, so she took all of the money she made from her mouse-breeding business and she visited the downtown Chanel boutique and bought a little black dress and shoes at a cost of $3,400, the amount she would receive for 8,200 mice. Rachel also visited a First Choice Haircutters outlet and asked for a makeover, because she had heard that all women love makeovers — and men find a woman who has been made over to be highly attractive. And then, having assessed her menstrual cycle, and dressed and groomed like a fertile and desirable human woman, she took a taxi to the airport hotel cocktail lounge because she has learned in Internet chat rooms that this is where people go to have flings. A "fling" is a human term to describe a zero-commitment, most often non-procreative, one-time-only sexual act. People in and around airports are usually experiencing a reduced sense of identity, and travellers like to flirt and experiment sexually in ways they would never do in their everyday environments.

So now Rachel is in a hotel cocktail lounge, using an out-of-date computer infected with multiple viruses that, when activated, trigger the noisy onscreen arrival of a Las Vegas slot machine depicting human vaginas that click into place along with an enticement to meet the right woman online, now, as long as a Visa, Amex, JTB, or MasterCard number is given. A quick search reveals that the web link is to a server in Belarus, a statistically unwise place to ship credit data.

Rachel is ready to begin her quest for motherhood.

———

Rachel saw the sunburned bartender and wondered how old he was. The bartender seemed to be in reasonable condition, but Rachel remembered that, as an employee, he was probably not inclined to be sexually disinhibited and thus in search of a fling. The bartender was speaking with a woman who looked about thirty-six — or perhaps thirty-four if she was addicted to alcohol. It's much easier to determine a woman's age, as nature is far more generous in offering visual prompts in that department. Seated at the bar was another man — early thirties? He appeared well-nourished, and Rachel tried to determine whether he was handsome. "Handsome" is the male equivalent of beautiful, and to neurotypicals handsomeness indicates good breeding stock. Having studied copies of *InStyle* magazine for years, trying to understand the language of looks, Rachel remained unable to calibrate any rules of attractiveness. On the other hand, the man at the bar, who had had two drinks since he had arrived, kept two large rolls of money in his jacket pocket. Rachel took this to mean he was rich and could be a good provider to a child.

The man looked at Rachel several times as she sat by her computer. She interpreted this as sexual interest and knew that it was her role to provide a countersignal, so she stood up and sauntered across the room in the manner of high-fashion models on TV.

On meeting the man — Luke — Rachel found him agreeable enough. Luke had a couple of drinks in him, so she knew he was more likely to laugh than if he was sober, and she hoped he wouldn't laugh. She hated laughter. Laughter was like a punctuation mark at the end of a sentence that reminded her she wasn't human.

And it was an awful sound, almost as annoying as crying babies.

A TV commercial showed a reindeer, so Luke brought up the subject of reindeer and Rachel thought she handled it very well. Then came the subject of religion, and she thought she held her own there, too. There was a conversational lull after Luke said something about sparrows, during which Rachel looked around the bar.

Luke then asked her what ideas she'd had that day, a question that seemed, even to Rachel, slightly out of the blue. Perhaps this was what she had read was called "foreplay."

"Is that a foreplay question, Luke?"

Luke smiled and almost made a laughing noise, but pulled back, which came as a relief. "Nope. Not foreplay. Our church is losing younger members, so they give us brochures on how to connect with young men and women. This one brochure told me that women love being asked that question, but they never get asked it. So I asked it."

Rachel was unable to understand the veneer of emotion coating Luke's voice. Bitterness? Decoding tone of voice was even harder for her than distinguishing one face from another. But she was almost paralyzed with pleasure at being called a woman, and the sensation made her rattle on more than she normally might as she answered his question. "I did have a new idea today. I was thinking about characters on science fiction TV shows who possess immortality, and how, when they're shot, the bullet wound quickly heals and they come back to life. Or, if they lose a limb, it grows back. But what about when they get blown up? From the blown-up chunks there's one piece that I suppose you would call the Master Chunk, which regenerates itself completely while the other body parts decompose. And then I got to thinking, what if an immortal character was blown up by an atomic bomb — which piece of the body would constitute the Master Chunk, and how would it reconstitute itself? And I figured that as long as one DNA molecule survived, then that's what the character would need in order to reconstitute and make itself immortal. But also, Luke, from what I've read, from the way the universe is constructed, and from the way atoms are built, the creation of life is an inevitability; in fact, the universe seems to have been built to be one enormous life-generating machine. So, even if the immortal's DNA was destroyed, its component atoms would still contain the inevitable destiny of forming a living being."

Luke looked at her. "Your thinking is way out there, lady."

"My doctor tells me I have multiple structural anomalies in my limbic system that affect my personality."

"You don't say."

"But what we call 'personality' is actually the result of a multifactorial gene process. A structural anomaly in my limbic system alone wouldn't account for the entirety of my personality."

"I suppose it wouldn't."

"I also have prosopagnosia, which is an inability to

tell faces apart, which, by association, also means I have trouble finding things inside other things, like finding faces or animal shapes in clouds."

"Yeah?"

"I also lack subjective qualities like humour and irony and . . ." Rachel then remembered from her normalcy training that people prefer it when you ask them a question after they've asked one of you — and besides, a list of her brain anomalies could take a good fifteen minutes to properly index, so she stopped discussing herself and asked Luke, "Have you had any ideas today, Luke?"

"Yes, I have. To fill the belief vacuum left by my lack of faith, I've decided that all I want from life is for people to like me or envy me — to either be my friend or wish they were me because I have a really cool life. But I've spent my life trying to get people to like me, and I'm not sure anyone does, and in any event, all it got me was nowhere. And I don't have anything in my life anyone could envy, so what's the point of either of those two wishes?"

Rachel stared at Luke. She was pretty sure now that it was bitterness she heard in his tone. She decided to return to her core mission of finding a desirable father for a child and said, "I see you're carrying large quantities of money. Is that something you do all the time?"

Luke spat out the ice cube he was bouncing about inside his mouth. "I stole it."

"Really?"

"Yup. I looted my church's construction fund."

"Oh," said Rachel. "Does that mean you're rich now?"

Player One

Cocktails and laughter — but what will come after? Humans have souls and machines have ghosts. Me — Player One — I'm actually more of a ghost than a soul, but it remains to be seen when I got here and how it happened.

At the moment, what matters most is that we learn what happens next in this story. What will happen next is that Rick will mix Karen her Singapore sling, and she will begin to drink it. Rick, forty-five dollars richer, will think about Leslie Freemont's Power Dynamics booklet: "Every second of our life we're reaching goals of some sort. Every single second of our lives we're crossing a finish line of some sort, with heaven's roaring cheers surrounding us as we win our way forward. In our smallest acts — crossing a street, peeling an apple, looking at our watch — it is as though we are accepting an Olympic ribbon to thunderous applause. The universe wants us to win. The universe makes sure we're winning, even when we lose." And then Rick will see a nondescript man wearing creepy sunglasses walk into the bar, saunter up to Karen, put his hand on her thigh, and say, "Hey there, Sunshine, I'm Warren."

Across the bar, Luke will visit the men's room and Rachel's mind will drift away. She will be thinking about the countless planets around the universe where life has, in all likelihood, formed. These life forms are probably carbon-based, but who knows? And chances are those other life forms won't look like humans. Absolutely not. The second-smartest animal on Earth is the New Caledonian crow. If those crows had longer lifespans and hands like Donald Duck, humans would have been obliterated eons ago. But if two equally smart species can coexist on the same planet, just imagine what other planets might have produced. There might even be entire planets that exist as one organism, like Teletubbies suns — or endless seas of prairie grass that together create one being. And of course, inevitably some of these life forms will have achieved sentience. Self-awareness. And Rachel will wonder if she'd be happier with these other life forms than she is with human beings. She will mention this idea to Luke, back from the men's room, and Luke will say, "Fine, fine, fine. But what I want to know is, do these aliens have an equivalent of free will? Do they perceive time differently? And most of all, what do they do for *money*?"

And there will then be big news from the TV set. And then Leslie Freemont will arrive. A photo will be taken. And then later, there will be rifle shots. And that is when there will be blood.

THE BEST OF THE REST OF YOUR LIFE

Karen

Karen's Internet date is lurching sideways quickly and catastrophically. She's frozen by the discrepancy between Warren's two Internet JPEGs (slightly game-show hosty, with a whiff of Old Spice) and his actual appearance (bantam roostery, with a pair of aviator glasses that make him resemble a repeat sex offender). And then there is the instant overfamiliarity when Warren places his slightly moist hand on her thigh, followed by another overfamiliarity of, "Hey there, Sunshine, I'm Warren." Warren — her highly anticipated date — is wearing the bland politician's smile of someone who knows that the bodies in the car trunk are, indeed, dead. Karen tries painting a happy face on this encounter, but almost against her will she is becoming a disembodied spectre floating above the meat version of herself, watching Warren order a Scotch and soda, then comment to her, "Quite the cocktail bar, huh? Everyone here looks like they're about to enter a witness relocation program." To this, Karen says (with a preachy tone in her voice that she has never liked in herself and that comes from nowhere), "Oh, please. Everyone knows the witness relocation program is a hoax."

"A hoax? How?"

"The FBI simply shoots the person and buries the body. If it's a family, then they shoot the family and bury the bodies. The fact that you never hear from them again perversely proves the success of the program."

Warren says, "I like that. I like *you.*"

At least Karen has no worries that Warren has overriding psych issues. She's seen enough patients go through her office to diagnose many of them simply by the way they react when she hands them a pen to fill out forms: paranoids jump; depressives stare at the pen; people off their meds begin free-association diatribes on ink. If people simply take the pen and use it, Karen knows they're probably going to make only a single visit. Warren's personality may be iffy, but there is no pathology in practice. She then, perversely, begins to wonder whether she is out of Warren's league or if he is out of hers. She wonders if Warren looks like the sort of man who would borrow your car and return it to you with several dents and no explanation — and on its seats would be a stain all the club soda on earth would be useless against. Karen has the woozy, regretfully sick morning-after sensation she has when she's been eBaying while drunk the night before. *What have I done, flying halfway across a continental land mass to meet a man I've known only electronically for two weeks, and only visually from two brazenly fraudulent JPEGs?*

Karen attempts humour: "Looks like we've hit the awkward patch pretty quickly."

Warren says, "The awkward patch usually happens a bit later," then catches himself, saying, "It's not like this is something I do all the time."

"How many times have you done this?"

Warren's pupils clench like sphincters. "I'm just messing with you, Sunshine."

Sunshine? Where is that coming from?

The bar's TV set displays South Carolina religious extremists protesting Halloween. Karen has the oddest feeling that, in dressing up to meet Warren, she's actually wearing the Halloween costume version of herself. She thinks of what a strange prospect it would be to throw a party themed "Come as the Halloween Costume Version of Yourself." She runs this idea past Warren, whose neck stiffens a bit, a reaction that informs Karen that he doesn't much enjoy abstract discussions.

"How do you mean, come as the Halloween version of myself?"

"I guess it would be dressing up like a highly amplified version of yourself."

"I don't get it."

"Well, you look at your wardrobe and your hair and you exaggerate everything and — I guess it'd be dressing

like a caricature of yourself. Like those unflattering political puppets on that English TV show." She pauses.
"Forget it." Warren's Scotch arrives, and she says, "I think
if people had real courage, they'd wear their Halloween
costume every day of the year. At the very least, you'd
make a lot more friends a lot more quickly. Like, 'Hey,
I like togas, too!' Or, 'Star Trek? I'm in.' Your costume
would be a means of filtering down to the people you'd
probably like the most."

Warren holds up his glass, forestalling further discussion, then says with a lewd smirk, "To us."

To us? Uh-oh.

Warren is mentally bedding Karen, and while almost
everyone wants to be thought of as sexy, Karen realizes
that the empowered sexiness she felt on the plane was
merely a manifestation of her new role as loser bait. She
looks at Rick, now speaking with the desperate-looking
trainwreck a few stools over. Suddenly, Rick's attractiveness has risen considerably; she feels embarrassed
being with Warren, as though she had accidentally sat
at the wrong lunch table in high school.

Warren asks, "How was your flight?"

"Fine. Lovely. Thanks."

The two begin reading the news crawl on the TV
screen. Karen realizes that the encounter isn't going
to be a story with a happy ending or even an unhappy
ending. It's simply going to be one more event in her
life that becomes a dot on a wall that won't connect
with any other dots to form a line with any beauty or

meaning. She feels like she's in a Discovery Channel clip showing wildebeests at a watering hole. The voice-over is telling viewers that wildebeests' lives don't have to be stories, the way people's lives do. Wildebeests only have to exist, lucky things, and they've done a good job of being alive on earth — as does pretty much everything on the planet save for human beings.

On the TV screen are three people in a flooded Midwest town, sitting on their roof having a barbecue and smiling as they wave to passing news copters. Karen feels a wash of jealousy: change entered the lives of these people unbidden. Change never happens in her own life, and while she'd gladly change her life herself, she has no idea in what *way* to change it. She feels like a taxidermied version of herself. *How quickly time passes, and how your mistakes add up one day to something less than what you wanted.*

"Warren, does your life ever feel like a story?"

Warren's body freezes. "A story? No. Yes. I don't know. I think so. Why?"

"Why? Because I think the story part of my life is over."

Karen had hoped a cocktail lounge would disinhibit her, make her more truthful in a randy way. She hoped that openness would turn into intimacy, that truth would lead to closeness, but instead the cocktail lounge is making her crabby as her repressed ideas and thoughts percolate to the surface.

Warren orders a second Scotch and watches a news clip about a small meteorite strike in Scotland. Karen thinks about Casey, age fifteen, walking into the kitchen last month, saying, "On December 4, in the year 65,370,112, a meteorite will strike the earth and all life will be killed." It makes Karen dizzy to think about the year 65,370,112, and yet that year will arrive as surely and relentlessly as the biweekly shopping flyers that clutter her front porch.

Casey described the next Ice Age to Karen as having "ice so thick and heavy it will puncture the earth's crust, generating molten blisters of nickel and bauxite and pitchblende. When that happens, the oceans will turn to steam. Life will end." How did Casey wind up being such a morbid child? Karen will never forget the moment her body froze at the Loblaws butcher counter a year back when Casey, out of the blue, asked if she could buy a pint of blood. Karen, in a rare moment of motherly composure, asked Casey why she might need this, and Casey said she and two friends wanted to invent a ritual.

"What kind of ritual?"

"I dunno. Something spooky."

"You have to be careful with rituals, Casey."

"Thanks for the advice, Mom."

"No, seriously. Sometimes with rituals you can open doors that can never be closed again. Not just with Ouija boards. Any ritual."

"Huh?" For once, Karen had entered Casey's world, and with bonus points for biting her tongue and not including the ritual of marriage along with the ritual use of Ouija boards.

Now Karen finds herself draining her drink and wanting another. But Rick is in the back area of the bar, with his head inside an ice machine. Karen wishes he would come back and say something that would lighten the mood. And get her another drink. The next drink might help things heal. Karen thinks back to just before Kevin asked for the divorce, when she asked him why he drank so much. He said he was trying to forget something, but he didn't know what it was. Kevin had been laid off and had entered a dark, scary brain-hole; he glumly forecasted a capitalist future in which all of humanity was in jail, and all people did was sit in their jail cells and shop online.

The news shifts to a story about cancer. Karen uses this opportunity to tell Warren, "You know, you've had cancer countless times in your life, except your body got rid of the condition and you never even knew you had cancer. What we call 'cancer' is actually a term for the cancers that stick around."

"You don't say."

"Interesting, huh?" Karen knows her cancer fun-fact would probably have sounded much better if it was read off a screen inside an email; spoken in real life, it makes her sound like a church lady. Life is so often a question of tone: what you hear inside your head versus what people end up reading or hearing from your mouth. Karen also hates her tendency to turn into a *Jeopardy!* game when she's nervous, and yet she begins prattling away: "And colds and flus are basically nature's way of training your body to fight cancer. You know the old maxim, *Never sick a day in their life, and then one day, pow!* People prone to colds and flus live longer. It's a fact."

Did I really just say, "It's a fact"?

Warren is quickly drifting away into TV land, and at that point it isn't like Karen wants Warren to stick around — but if he's going to be leaving, Karen wants the exit to be on her terms. She needs just that eensiest bit of control, so she can emerge emotionally intact from this random situation. She hammers the final nail into the coffin of her Internet date: "Warren, if you were a contestant on *Jeopardy!*, what would your six favourite categories be?"

Under his breath, Warren mutters, "Jesus H. Christ. Are you a talker, or what?"

Karen's life may well not be a story. She knows this now. She knows that seeing your life as a story is probably just some corny residue left over from the era of Hollywood studios, and of a society full of newspapers and magazines kept robust through healthy advertising revenue, as well as middle-class book clubs in which overeducated people fake-read the second half of the book and pretend they know more about the evening's wine than they actually do.

Karen has noticed that young people no longer seem to care if their lives are stories. Not Casey, and not that little pervert on the flight earlier that afternoon. He'd probably no more view his life as a story than he would view his life as that of a sea cucumber. He and Casey inhabit a world of screen grabs, website hits, and precisely tabulated numbers of friends and enemies. Why, that little pervert on the plane would see Karen only as a hot mom who gave him a bit of sass. Karen knows that her photo is probably now on Facebook and she's been labelled a cougar. And guaranteed, the kid on the plane would have no pity were he to see Karen in a cocktail lounge with a failed Internet hookup, the makeup in the wrinkles at the corners of her eyes by now crumbling like the pyramids, all illusions of youth vanishing. Where did the years go? *When time is used up, does it go to some kind of place like a junkyard? Or down a river like the waters beneath Niagara Falls? Does time evaporate and turn into rain and start all over again?*

It feels odd for Karen to be a person without a story, like so many other people out there now, left marooned at a certain age without a narrative engine to pull them through their days. In the old days, she could at least have adopted a role within the community: the divorcée cautionary tale; the tough old broad who . . . she doesn't even know. The tough old broad who makes birdhouses out of licence plates? The tough old broad who fills X number of years until her death doing nothing of consequence until science, genetics, nutrition, and life decisions collectively fail and take her to the inevitable end?

Karen sat on her bar stool, watching Warren, clad in his repeat-sex-offender eyewear, watching the bar's TV. Maybe he wasn't so bad after all. *No, dear God, no, this can't be happening.* A part of Karen was suddenly disgusted by the part of her that was oddly turned on by the part of Warren's personality that was actually kind of base and mean and sexy — the part of him that had charmed and seduced her into a cocktail lounge 2,500 kilometres away from home. Online he was such a charmer. Karen had thought he would touch her body gently and methodically — this body that needs some hands on it quickly — as though he were at the bank counting a stack of twenties.

Warren's hands were rubbing the rim of his highball glass. Rick appeared and, to her surprise, handed Karen her second drink of the afternoon. Warren asked, "Feeling better?" and, oddly, she was. And that was the point when Warren yelled out, "Jesus H. Christ, oil just went to $250 a barrel!"

Warren and Karen sat transfixed, watching a CP24 newscaster interrupt regular news to show images of OPEC leaders fleeing a São Paulo hotel dining room after a large explosion of some sort. The news crawl beneath it reported light crude oil listing on the Dow at US$251.16 a barrel.

Warren said to Karen, "Is that for real? Holy *shit*. Just like they said."

Rick looked at Karen and asked with genuine amazement, "They? Who's they?"

Karen said, "Actually, it was just this one guy named Hubbert."

Rick asked, "Who's Hubbert?"

Warren said, "Dr. Marion King Hubbert was a Shell Oil geologist who predicted in 1956 that US domestic oil production would peak around 1970 and that global production would peak around 2000."

"And . . . ?"

Warren continued, "That production peak is called Hubbert's Peak. And it looks like it's finally happened."

As an aside, Karen said, "The 1970s oil shock set his calendar back by a decade. But he was right."

"How on earth do you people know this?"

"It's kind of weird," Karen said. "We met in a — God, this is so embarrassing — a Peak Oil Apocalypse chat room."

"Man," Warren said, "wouldn't Hubbert freak to see oil over $250 a barrel."

Rick said, "You mean you two actually did meet in a Peak Oil Apocalypse chat room?"

Warren said, "Yeah, so what? There are a lot of collapsitarians like me out there."

Karen, slightly embarrassed, added, "I was in a dark patch — visiting the doom and gloom sites — we all do that sometimes. God knows there are enough of them."

"Look!" Warren shouted. "Look at the crawl: oil just hit $290 a barrel!"

And then the bar's power went out, just long enough for everyone to think, *Oooooooooooh*. And then the power returned, but the TV's cable connection was dead.

Rick

Rick looks over at the high-tipping Mr. Trainwreck now trying to pick up Miss Ginger Ale, or . . . or what, exactly, is going on there? What's the deal with Miss Ginger Ale? None of her gestures make any sense to Rick; she seems to have some kind of genetic malfunction; she's like one of those Japanese department store greeting robots he's seen on YouTube.

There is a lull in their conversation, so he heads over that way, and Miss Ginger Ale looks at Rick and says, "Did you know that every human being on earth is related to a single woman who existed 160,000 years ago in a place we now commonly call France?"

"Seriously?" said Rick. "Related to every person on earth?"

"Yes."

"Man, she must have been one total slut."

Mr. Trainwreck snorts, then swallows the Scotch in his mouth and has a belly laugh, which seems to confuse Miss Ginger Ale. But Rick has done his job as bartender — enlivening the lives of his guests — and he walks to the rear of the bar and inspects the ice machine, which has been on the fritz of late. While fiddling with its guts, Rick is, of course, wondering, *Where is Leslie Freemont? Is Leslie Freemont bailing on his meeting with me?* Rick looks at his phone: Leslie is fifteen minutes late. *Where is he! Where is he! Where is he! And for that matter, where is all the gardening equipment that was stolen along with my truck? And for that matter, where is the better version of myself that I've been hoping for since high school?*

In moments like these, when time slows to a crawl, Rick wishes he could start drinking again. *Man, I loved booze. Booze made me feel the way being in a womb must feel. If fetuses aren't getting alcohol, what, exactly, are they getting in there that makes the womb everybody's dream vacation spot?*

Rick catches his reflection on the freezer's shiny surface. *Uh-oh — my teeth! My teeth are dirty! Leslie Freemont will see my teeth and deem me deficient!* Rick, like many people, tends, accurately or not, to blame his teeth for many of the perceived wrongs in his life. He slips into the bathroom and quickly overbrushes his molars, and blood drips into the sink's chipped white ceramic bowl. Rick rinses out his mouth gunk and returns to the bar. When he sips from a cold cup of coffee, his mouth detects a familiar and undesirable taste: that of cooked liver. *Huh? Why am I tasting liver?* And then he realizes that what he's tasting is dead blood cells, which is the reason liver tastes like liver, because the liver is the body's blood purifying system. This observation amuses Rick, but it also reinforces his practice of not eating any piece of meat that once had a job: livers, kidneys, thymus glands . . . wings. Rick will only eat *meat* meat. Of course, within Rick's universe of unemployed meat, hot dogs and hamburgers are exempt from his rule, his thinking being that if you chop up something finely enough and turn it into a geometric shape, it will always become quite palatable.

Rick looks at Karen; her Internet date is clearly tanking. He knows he could put the pair of them out of their misery and discuss the weather with them, but the only way people are going to learn is from their mistakes.

In any event, Rick likes the way he feels right now and wants to keep it going. It feels like Christmas morning. When he woke up this morning, the day felt different than it normally does. Usually, when he opens his eyes, there are a few glorious moments before he remembers who he is, where he is, and what he's become. And after that he's Wile E. Coyote, running off the cliff and suddenly realizing he's going to pancake onto the desert floor below. And this is when his automatic thinking kicks in, the tape loop along the lines of: *Maybe I didn't try hard enough to wake up this morning. If only I was more awake, more alert, I could look closely enough at the world and a magic revelation would be mine — if only I could wake up just that little bit more. Dammit, I spend my whole life looking and looking and looking at the world, but I guarantee it, the moment I move my head away from my patch of ground will be the exact moment the earth cracks open — and if I'd been watching, for just that one second, I'd have seen the core of the planet, molten and white.*

But wait — today with Leslie Freemont, I will wake up that extra little bit!

Leslie Freemont will widen Rick's point of view and make Rick feel good about himself. For example,

Leslie says it doesn't matter where in the universe you are, all emotions are the same, a universal constant — and yes, we as humans get to experience them all. It's what makes us superior to animals. Leslie is awesome smart. Leslie is like a glamorous train passing through the landscape, people waving at him all the way. Rick, on the other hand, is a bus. People don't wave at buses. Wait — he's not even a bus; he's a stalled car with a flat tire on the side of a gravel road nobody ever uses. And his passenger window is broken and replaced by plastic dry-cleaning bags and clear packing tape.

Rick looks across the bar and witnesses Karen's misery. Suddenly he feels magnanimous. He takes pity on Karen, with her obviously awkward chit-chat, and decides to mix her another Singapore sling. He looks up the drink in his mixology book and is newly shocked by the list of ingredients; he can't believe the crap people used to put in their bodies in the twentieth century.

As he mixes the drink, Rick's thoughts return to Leslie Freemont. Won't young Tyler be proud when he finds out his father has a dynamic new way of seeing the world! Up until now, Rick has been passionless, but the Power Dynamics Seminar System has made him realize how unimpressive his old life was. The Power Dynamics Seminar System is a bright new sun casting a trillion new shadows in his brain, and his Tyler will see him in a whole new light!

Rick then imagines a magic custody afternoon sometime in the future in which Pam will walk into the room just as he's telling Tyler about Leslie Freemont. Pam will say something like, "Rick, I'm holding a do-I-give-a-shit-ometer in my hand, and the needle's not moving. Shut up. Your afternoon with Tyler is over. Go back to your crappy little basement apartment and get hosed and curse at the universe."

Rick takes a sip of the Singapore sling. *Rick . . . what the hell!* This is not the recurring dream about slipping that Rick has a few times a week. This is real life. *Oh dear God, what was I thinking? Oh jeez-Louise, a fourteen-month AA chip right down the toilet. Tyler can never find out about this.*

But the genie is out of the bottle, and the genie is rushing to the reptile stem of Rick's brain. Instead of feeling buzzy and great, Rick feels weakness and fear and self-loathing and kind of like he's falling into a hole. He remembers walking through a local graveyard as a child, with three friends. He told them he had the ability to see corpses buried in the ground, that they had a radioactive green colour, and this impressed his friends no end. And then he convinced himself that he actually had this power, and he walked through parks and rode along highways imagining radioactive dead green bodies everywhere. One morning he looked at his face in the mirror and he was green, and he honestly believed he was dead. And that's how he feels now.

He pours the drink down the sink, runs to the ice machine, and sticks his head inside, trying to cool the burning shame. The sub-zero mist enters his nostrils, freezer-burning his membranes. His sweat is cold. Leslie Freemont is going to meet Rick at the bottom of a shame spiral; this is not what the day was supposed to be like.

Work.

Right.

Rick mixes a new Singapore sling. Work will save him in the end. He takes the drink to Karen, but her eyes inform him that she no longer needs rescuing . . . perhaps her tide has turned; maybe she'll score after all. Then Karen and Warren see something on the TV and go all chimpy about, of all things, the price of crude oil. *Crude oil?* Rick learns that they met in an online crude oil discussion group. Who on earth hooks up in an online discussion group about crude oil?

And then the power goes out.

And then the power comes back on.

And then the TV stops working.

And then Leslie Freemont enters the cocktail lounge.

———

Leslie entered the lounge like a taller, thinner, studlier version of the Kentucky Fried Chicken colonel: white-suited and platinum-haired, with strong, fluoridated teeth and a Greek shipping magnate's tan. He sized up Rick at the cash register, reached out his hand, and said, "I'm Leslie Freemont. You must be Rick."

Rick had no idea what to say. Everyone in the bar

was staring at him. He was not a good improviser and felt a stinging blush come on. "Yes, I am."

"Hey, Rick, welcome to the best of the rest of your life!" Right behind Leslie fluttered a personal assistant, Tara, manoeuvring two pieces of wheeled luggage, each with a mind of its own. "Rick, this is Tara. Tara, Rick."

Hellos were exchanged, and Leslie said, "Rick, I bet you feel *great*!" Leslie was like a walking exclamation mark. Everything about him exuded confidence, life force, and energy. Rick wanted what Leslie had, and he wanted it now. He asked, "Leslie, can I get you a drink?"

"Not for me. But maybe young Tara here could use a pick-me-up — just kidding. Nothing for Tara — she's on the job. And Tara, be careful with the smaller leather bag there; I bought it at Heathrow and I'm trying to keep it clean for next month's cruise." Leslie looked at Rick. "And I was kidding about not wanting a drink. I'll have what this gentleman here is having." He motioned to Warren's Scotch and soda. He stuck out a manly hand to Warren, and then to Karen: "Leslie Freemont . . . Leslie Freemont. Ah, my drink. Thank you, Rick. Wait — I'm one of those folks who has a peanut allergy. In all seriousness, is this glass clean?"

"Fresh from the shelf."

"Merci beaucoup." He took a sip. "Ah, rich, nourishing booze. With the first drink comes the truth, with the second drink comes wishful thinking, and with the third drink come the lies. What would we do without sweet, nourishing alcohol?" He raised his highball glass and bellowed, "A toast!" Even Miss Ginger Ale raised her glass. "Here's a toast to everyone on earth who's ever been eager, no, *desperate* for even the smallest sign that there exists something finer, larger, and more miraculous about our inner selves than we could ever have supposed. Here's to all of us, reaching out our hands to people everywhere, reaching out to pull them from the icebergs in which they stand frozen, to pull them through the burning hoops of fire that make them frightened, and to pull them through the brick walls that block their paths. Let us reach out to shock and captivate these people into new ways of thinking."

Leslie's toast took a moment to sink in, but was then greeted by a hearty "Cheers!"

Miss Ginger Ale said, "I've seen you on TV."

"You probably have," said Leslie. "My new TV project airs in the coveted midnight-to-one-a.m. slot, weeknights, in two major North American markets."

"I watch your show while I work in my laboratory mouse-breeding facility."

That line stopped everyone dead. Mr. Trainwreck got things moving again. "So you have a TV show, not an infomercial?" he asked.

"Edutainment," said Leslie. "I like to call it a 'lifeomercial.' I'm not on TV primarily to sell — first and foremost, I'm there to fix people's lives."

"Are you some form of doctor?" asked Miss Ginger Ale.

"No, ma'am, just a humble shepherd."

"So you're an evangelist?" asked Mr. Trainwreck.

"Not as such," Leslie replied. "But if helping people in pain is a crime, then I guess you'd call me a criminal." Leslie turned to Rick. "Young man, Tara and I are on the move today, but we cherish this chance to have met you."

"What time is your flight?" Rick asked.

Leslie raised an eyebrow at Tara, who quickly blurted, "We have to board in ninety minutes."

"So," said Leslie, "I'm afraid we have only a brief moment for a photo. I trust you're still going to invest in the full Leslie Freemont Power Dynamics program."

"Of course," said Rick, who at that moment would gladly have donated all of his internal organs to invest in the full Leslie Freemont Power Dynamics Seminar System.

"Wonderful."

"Do you have the payment?" asked Tara.

Rick handed it to her. "It's cash. Exactly $8,500. You can count it if you like."

"No need," said Leslie, being good cop to Tara's bad cop. "Come around to this side of the bar while Tara readies the camera."

Rick hopped over the bar in one leap, barely missing a Rubbermaid tray containing lemon wedges and maraschino cherries, then took off his apron in one gesture. "I am so stoked!"

"And your great adventure," said Leslie, "has only just begun. Tara?"

Leslie put his arm around Rick and told him to say the word "win." "It gives you the best smile of all."

Tara snapped a digital photo. Leslie grabbed the camera. "It's a beauty. Good work, Tara." He pumped Rick's hand. "Rick, we'll email you the JPEG."

"Thanks, Leslie."

Leslie chugged his Scotch. "And now we're off, and thank you for your commitment to my vision. A FedEx with the full program will arrive at this address in two days." Leslie looked up at the room. "People — nice to have met you all. Welcome to the best of the rest of your life."

And with that, Leslie and Tara were gone, a little bit too quickly, giving Rick just the briefest whiff of suspicion that Leslie's interest in Rick's future success and mental livelihood might not have been entirely spiritual.

Luke

It wasn't just the Bake Sale Committee's pissy reaction to Luke's Rapture joke that made him reach his tipping point and loot the parish coffers and abandon his flock. Something else happened. When the Bake Sale meeting was over, Luke walked past the out-of-tune baby upright piano and up the rear staircase, which smelled of old textbooks. He went into his office and locked the door. He sat in his wooden chair, which overlooked the rear parking lot, where the women were milling about their cars and gossiping, most likely about him. He turned off his cellphone and took his land line off the hook and watched the women leave. Then he looked to the side of the window, where a crow on a telephone wire was having a deep, vigorous preening session, feathers akimbo, *groom, groom, groom*. After finishing its routine, the crow fluffed out its feathers, pooped, and then yawned.

It yawned?

Birds yawn?

Luke found it interesting that birds yawn. Some people would have us believe that birds and human beings evolved from one common ancestor six hundred million years ago — which would mean that yawning goes back six hundred million years — as does, Luke supposed, preening and grooming and battling for turf and seeking out mates and . . .

. . . suddenly the idea of sharing a common ancestor made more sense than the thought of being created in six days — more than the notion of Creation itself. Luke's loss of faith was that quick. He'd always feared it, but he had thought it would be a long, drawn-out process. He should have known it would happen in an instant. From years of tending his flock, he knows that most big moments in life and death are quick — those key moments that define us probably fill less than three minutes altogether.

The next morning — this morning — Luke drove to the bank and made small talk with Cindy the teller, who had a port wine birthmark on her chin, after which he withdrew the church's savings and went to the airport to catch the first flight he could get to a big city, which happened to be Toronto, where he now sits with a crazy robot-woman supermodel.

On his bar stool, his pockets brimming with cash, Luke feels as though he radiates darkness as surely as the sun radiates light. Luke still believes that we are all, at every moment of our lives, equally on the brink of all sins, except that now, in a world without faith, sin has no ramifications; it's just something humans do.

Luke sits with the flawlessly beautiful Rachel. The TV screen shows the remains of a Florida zoo recently pummelled by a hurricane. An array of animals and birds stand amid and on top of broken walls and mangled metal, yet none of them knows it's wreckage; it's merely the world. Luke feels old and lost. He felt lost when he was young, too, but back then he felt lost in his own special way. Now he feels lost in the same way everybody else does.

Luke turns to Rachel and asks, "Have you ever had a vision?"

"I don't understand your question, Luke."

"A vision — a picture in your mind that's not real life, but it's not a dream, either — it's something you see that you know is true and you know is going to happen."

"Have you?"

"Once. Last summer. I was with my sister and her kids, at some lake. The kids were driving me nuts, so I went off on my own and got lost in the scrub — it's easier to get lost than you think — and I ended up on a sandbar down the lake. I was thirsty, but I didn't want to drink the water because it probably had bear shit and skunk shit in it, and who knows what else, so I was dehydrated, and I found this sandbar and then, *wham!* I had this vision. I fell to my knees and I saw a wash of light, and then I saw a fleet of dazzling metal spaceships, like bullets aimed at the sun, and I wanted to walk towards them and get inside one and leave everything behind. I'd had a vision, the only vision I've ever had, but it told me nothing and offered no comfort or guidance."

"Were the spaceships built by humans or by aliens?"

"I hadn't thought of that. Humans, I think." He looks at the gorgeous but unreadable Rachel. "Do you believe in aliens?"

"I think that all subatomic particles are designed specifically to generate life the first moment they possibly can. In our case, it happens to be based on DNA. On other planets, other designs will have occurred. Perhaps stacked rings or some other linear structure. Scientists now believe that life started on earth not just once, but many times, until it continued to become the forms we currently experience. Even if you took a planet full of nitrous sludge and did everything to hinder life's development, it would still evolve." Rachel pauses. "Actually, Luke, sometimes I *do* see pictures in my head — when I'm working in the garage and have been overconcentrating in bright light. They don't make any sense, but I do see them . . . I once had this vision that a mountainside collapsed and buried me. While I watched it start to fall down, I wasn't at all frightened. I knew that the weight of the soil and rocks would make me feel safe and protected."

Luke's pupils dilated upon hearing of Rachel's visions. Something she had said had emotionally affected him. "Does your vision mean anything, you think?"

"No. Perhaps only that I had curry for dinner and its effect on my stomach is psychoactive. But the landslide dream did make me stop worrying about death."

Luke looked at her face closely. "Maybe someday you might become a poet."

"I don't understand poetry."

"That doesn't surprise me, but you probably have other things going for you. I can tell." Luke polishes off what remains in his glass and sighs. "Rachel, I wish everything would just end. I think I've had just about as much of this world as I'm able to take. I'm pooped."

"Is that what people call 'a cry for help'? Should I notify a local suicide hotline of your intentions?"

"No! Jesus! Have another sip of your drink."

Rick passes by, and Rachel looks at Rick and says, "Did you know that every human being on earth is related to a single woman who existed 160,000 years ago in a place we now commonly call France?"

"Seriously?" said Rick. "Related to every person on earth?"

"Yes."

"Man, she must have been one total slut."

Luke almost chokes on his Scotch, but then manages to swallow it and bursts out laughing. Rick heads off to the back of the bar.

Rachel looks confused. She asks Luke, "What's wrong with being a slut? I would think society would welcome fertile women fully enthusiastic about reproducing with a wide variety of genes so as to propagate the species in a genetically healthy and sensible manner."

Luke looks at Rachel. "That's certainly one way of viewing things."

"Luke, are you single or married?"

Luke says, "I'm single," but doesn't know if this is the right answer if he's going to make it with Rachel. Being single is a self-fulfilling situation. *Why are you single? Something must be wrong. I'll pass, thank you.* It's slightly easier for single men than for single women, but it sends out an awkward signal nevertheless. Single means lonely, and lonely is scary, as Luke knows all too well from years of counselling his flock. Luke is lonely, too, but only when he thinks about time and growing old alone. Luke is afraid of getting hurt, but he also knows that if too much time passes you miss out on the opportunity to be hurt by other people. To a younger Luke this sounded like luck; to an older Luke this sounds like a quiet tragedy.

The TV screen shows more of the trashed Florida zoo, waist-deep in water. Luke once thought time was like a river, and that it always flowed at the same speed, no matter what. But now he believes that time has floods, too — it simply isn't a constant anymore. Twenty thousand dollars in his pockets, and Luke feels like he's in the flood.

Luke asks, "What about you? Single?"

"Yes. Irregularities in the insula, cingulate, and inferior frontal parts of the brain make me unable to have what neurotypical people such as you call a 'relationship.' I enjoy situations that are familiar to me, and if that means having a person around me, then I suppose that's fine. But it's not something I crave or seek. I also have 630 people following my ongoing blog on the subject of mouse breeding. One might consider them, if not partners, then friends. They constitute my community."

"You don't say."

"But this may change. The brain grows ten thousand new cells every day of its life — but unless you use them, they dissolve back into your brain."

"Serves them right," says Luke. "Okay, Rachel, what do you crave or seek from life, then?"

"I would like to become impregnated by an alpha

male so that I can prove to my father that I am, in fact, a human being and not a monster or an alien."

Luke looks at Rachel. "Let me buy you another drink."

Rick returns from the bar's rear area. Luke watches him mix a complicated cocktail and take a sip from it — are bartenders allowed to do that? — then inexplicably pour it out and flee into the back, returning a half-minute later looking like hell. Crystal meth? Crack? Luke thinks, *Well, it's an airport bar. Who wouldn't?* An airport isn't even a real place. It's a pit stop, an in-between area, a "nowhere," a technicality — a grudging intrusion into the seamless dream of transcontinental jet flight. Airports are where you go right after you've died and before you get shipped off to wherever you're going next. They're the present tense crystallized into aluminum, concrete, and bad lighting.

Luke watches as Rick mixes another drink and hands it to Karen — and then oil hits $250 a barrel. Even Rachel's ears perk up at that news. She tells Luke, "That means a tank of gas for a typical North American–made sedan will cost roughly $300."

Luke remembers driving to the airport to catch his flight to freedom. The gas at the pumps back home was a buck and a half per litre. Would they even be open now? Just then, the power goes out. When it returns ten seconds later, the TV is white, fuzzy snow.

———

Amidst all of the action and all the cocktails, what was troubling Luke most was the paradigm shift inside his head. Just yesterday he had believed that after he died he would go to a place called Eternity. Now all he had to look forward to was a paltry place called the future. The future is not the same thing as Eternity. Eternity is everything and nothing. In the future, things that were already happening keep going on, but without you.

Because Luke no longer believed in Eternity, he had only the future. The day after he died there might be a really huge, terrific party and he wouldn't be there to attend. A year or two later they might tear down his old neighbourhood and raise skyscrapers shaped like handguns. In two million years, squirrels might have developed frontal cortices and enslaved the world. Who was to say? Luke would never know, because he'd be dead and would have left all known time streams.

Of course, there was no guarantee that dwellers in Eternity would get peeks back into their pre-eternal world. Luke always did wonder what the point of that would be — so they could gloat? So they could settle bets? So they could see the latest *Star Wars* instalment? No matter how he looked at it, there remained something petty about Eternals looking backwards. No. Once you're gone, you'll never find out who won the World Series, who wore what to the Oscars, or whether your kids went on to cure cancer or murder Girl Guides. Luke is on the cusp of ordering another round of drinks for himself and Rachel when Leslie Freemont enters the building.

Rachel turned to look at Leslie Freemont. "I've seen that man on TV."

"It's that fraud — Freeman . . . Freemont — what the hell is he doing here?"

"Being on television would make him a good genetic donor, would it not? And his skin is tanned. He must be a sportive outdoors type."

Luke was surprised by how angered he was that Leslie Freemont had become a threat to his potential hookup with Rachel. "Suntan? That's fake-and-bake, trust me, and the TV thing? It's infomercials for some quack self-help cult."

"He seems confident and virile."

"He's a complete hoax."

Yet, of course, the two continued watching as Leslie seduced the western side of the bar. They even participated in a toast with the man. And after the briefest of visits, capped by a quickie snapshot, Leslie and his assistant were gone.

Rachel

Rachel is trying to establish whether Luke might be a suitable father for her child — a man with a wad of cash in his pocket who recently stopped believing in religion. Religion strikes Rachel as reproduction-neutral, but Luke says he once had a vision of a spaceship headed heavenward — perhaps he is a poet? Neurotypical people are an endless source of puzzles. Religion is one of the biggest.

In any event, when oil hits $250 a barrel, Rachel's brain senses a threat to her body, making her amygdala kick in to create a duplicate recording of her cocktail lounge experience, which, afterwards, she will be able to scan for data that she can learn from, to protect herself in a similar situation. Her brain's double recording of the event will make it feel as if it happened in slow motion. The doubling of neural information simulates the lengthening of time, and because Rachel is different, she is able to keep dual recordings of intense events running far longer than neurotypicals. Thus, Rachel will be able to revisit the arrival and departure of Leslie Freemont and his assistant, Tara.

Rachel is grateful for Leslie's cocoa butter tan and white outfit and white hair, as it gives him distinctive non-facial characteristics that allow her to recognize him without having to resort to eyes, ears, and mouth. She has no idea how the rest of the world can tell each other apart. What would be wrong with everyone wearing name tags? It wouldn't be difficult or expensive — and yet nobody is interested.

Rachel is also relieved that nobody in the cocktail lounge makes laughing noises when she announces that she breeds white mice for a living. She received a lot of the laughing noises back in high school, when she first went into business. As she walked past other students, they'd say, "*Squeak-squeak*" — a bad imitation of the noise white mice make, which is, in fact, almost no noise at all. The laughing noise usually means her day is going to be just that much harder.

Once Leslie leaves, the group of five clusters around the truly dreadful computer in search of news. Warren seizes control of the keyboard. Nobody else seems to care, but Rachel can tell that Warren isn't actually that good with computers. "Fricking hell, it's asking me to download some kind of patch." Warren's tone reminds Rachel of her father and thus her mating mission.

Her current situation may be bewildering and slightly scary, but Rachel presses forward, saying, "Push CONTROL-4 to override that request."

It works.

Karen says, "Go to CNN.com. Hurry! Hurry!" But Warren is klutzy and hits the wrong keys, triggering a cluster of frozen windows.

Rick asks Rachel, "You — what's your name?"

"My name is . . . Rachel."

"Rachel, take over from this guy."

Warren rebels, saying, "Well, my name is Warren, and screw you. I'm almost in."

"Warren," Rick says, "my grandmother's more web-savvy than you."

Karen says, "Both you men, just shut up. Wait — CNN's on the screen."

They look at the CNN page, which is shattering into digital fragments. During its two seconds onscreen, the group sees the words OIL HITS $350 and NEW INFO SHEDS LIGHT ON ANNA NICOLE SMITH'S DRUG SUICIDE.

Then the connection dies and the server asks if they'd like to test a new Microsoft upgrade for their system.

"Jesus H. Christ," barks Warren. "This hunk of crap probably has a dot matrix printer, too."

"Actually," Rick says, "it does, but I can't find paper with tractor-tread holes on the sides anymore."

Rachel begins thinking about a world in which oil costs $350 a barrel, and it's not a world the people she knows would want to live in — not exactly a world of empty roads and starving masses, but getting there. Fewer planes. Fewer vegetables and fruits. Anarchy. Crime. Maybe some suicides. There may no longer be a need for high-quality white mice in this world, and then what will she do? For a brief moment she thinks of the pizza-sized black circles cartoon characters throw onto the ground — portable holes — which they jump into to escape difficult situations. In her mind, that's where people go when they die: down Daffy Duck's cartoon hole. How comforting to have a wide array of cartoon friends to meet you on the other side! Cartoons were introduced to Rachel as a means of explaining the concept of humour, but she ended up preferring cartoons over real life because in cartoons she could at least tell whose face was saying what. She hasn't watched a film in years. But there, in the stress of the bar, she wishes she had a cartoon hole she could escape into. But no — she's on a mission, and this is no time to bail.

Warren was yelling at the hard drive, and Karen was yelling at Warren for yelling at the machine. The two reminded Rachel of her parents, but she knew from Luke that they had met only an hour beforehand. Perhaps they were ... *What is the term?* ... a match made in heaven and ought to reproduce as quickly as possible.

Warren clearly held Rick responsible for the lounge's lame computer and for his inability to get a cellphone connection. "How hard can it be for a hotel lounge to have decent wireless? You've got nothing to do all day but make three margaritas and stick some bar mix in a bowl. You'd think you'd have time to find a computer that works."

"Right, Warren. I'll put it on the agenda at the next board meeting, right after my PowerPoint presentation to implement a chain-wide series of planet-friendly green initiatives."

"There's no other computer in this place?"

"In the hotel's main office. Be my guest and go use it."

"Smartass. Wait — I think I've got CNN again." The screen's address bar indicated a connection to the website, and the loading bar indicated it was about to appear. Then an ad for Tropicana orange juice popped up. Warren was incensed. "Jesus H. Christ."

Rick said, "Why don't we let Rachel give this a try?"

"Yeah, sure," Warren said. "I get it. Out with the old, in with the young."

Karen said, "Warren, just move. Rachel, try and get us online here."

Rachel sat and executed some keystrokes that unclogged much of Warren's mess. She considered rebooting but decided not to risk it. As she tried reaching various news websites, she reasoned that if oil was now $350 a barrel, most airline flights would soon be grounded. Gas stations would be emptied in minutes, and all grocery stores gutted. She asked Rick, "Do you have a radio?"

"Just in my truck," Rick said.

"We should go out and listen to it," Rachel said. "We'll get the news faster that way."

"No!" said Warren. "We are going to get the real facts online. Keep trying, Rachel."

Karen said, "I'd rather listen to the radio right now."

Rick said, "Me too."

Warren said, "Then go. I'm getting my information the modern way. Radio is for losers."

Rick said, "Right then, the truck's out back."

Luke decided to join them. They walked out the lounge's glass door, which was covered in blistering, peeling sun-screening material, and into the baking afternoon.

The air outside seemed much quieter than it had when Rachel entered the cocktail lounge. Then she realized that the relative silence stemmed from the absence of air traffic into and out of the airport. Rick said, "This way," and they walked to an aging black Dodge Ram pickup and opened the doors. The four of them got inside. Rick put the key in the ignition to activate the radio.

Luke said, "At the moment it'll probably cost you five bucks just to idle the car. God only knows what the pump price is right now. Airport's pretty quiet, too."

Rachel said, "I doubt the airlines can afford to fly. People booked on flights today won't be going anywhere. Probably not tomorrow, either. Maybe never."

Karen snapped, "Quiet, all of you. Rick, turn on the effing radio."

"Yes, ma'am."

They tuned in to the local AM news/traffic station. The normally cheery banter was gone, replaced by a very factual reading of incoming bulletins.

. . . the Niagara Falls crossings have been closed until further notice, and authorities have requested that civilians not go near the half-kilometre buffer zone. In downtown Toronto, we have confirmation that the

Gardiner Expressway has been closed after a series of noises we're told sounded like explosions. Listener phone-ins report what seems to be a riot at the Eaton Centre, but 680 News has yet to confirm . . .

Suddenly there was a flash on the horizon, followed by a booming sound that raced through the truck's cab like a banshee. Its four passengers looked up and saw a small mushroom cloud maybe five kilometres from the lounge.

Luke said, "Holy crap!"

Rachel instantly analyzed it: "It's not nuclear. It's chemical. Oil, most likely, given the black smoke at the bottom."

Warren rushed out of the lounge and looked at the fireball. He looked around, saw his barmates in the truck, and shouted, "Holy crap!" Rachel wondered what it was about extreme disaster that made people invoke both religion and excrement — bookends to mark the polarities of the human condition?

Rick and Karen tried using their cellphones, without luck. Luke was entranced by the chemical cloud — he just kept looking at it, mesmerized, as if it were the face of God.

Warren started to head their way, but three steps from the lounge door his head jerked sideways, with what looked like an explosion of red feathers but was obviously, when Rachel thought about it for a millionth of a second, blood.

Because Rachel's amygdala was still double-processing, this event, like everything else that had happened since the price of oil hit $250, occurred in slow motion.

A second pulse of blood shot from the centre of Warren's chest, and even before he hit the ground, it was obvious that he was dead.

Time stopped. Karen screamed. The sun suddenly seemed a dozen times too bright. Rick swatted the cab's passengers down with his arm: "Everyone, *down!*"

Rachel responded to the violence with the fugue state her brain often deployed when overwhelmed, a state that made the meaner boys in her class at school call out during fire alarms, "Rachel's gone to her Happy Place." Rachel thinks there's a lot to be said for Happy Places, and if the bullies and teasers knew what the Happy Place was like, they'd not only leave her alone, they'd be begging her for directions. When Rachel goes to hers it's like being in a noisy, crowded restaurant with music blaring, when suddenly the music is turned off and everybody leaves. There is calm. She can be objective. She can analyze. She feels free and powerful — it's as if suddenly she's been given the search result for every keyword ever put into Google. She comes away from her Happy Place calm and unworried, as if her brain has had a chicken white-meat sandwich and a glass of milk.

Sitting there in the truck with Rick, Karen, and Luke, Rachel was in her Happy Place, and she remembered something her mathematics teacher had once said to the class: "When you think about all the coincidences that might have happened but never did, then you begin to look at the universe in a different way. At any moment, trillions of sextillions of coincidences might have happened in your daily life, and yet, upon reflection, you realize that coincidences almost never occur. Coincidences are so rare as to be remarkable when they *do* occur. Coincidences are, in fact, so rare that it's almost as if the universe is engineered solely to keep them at bay. So when a coincidence or something extraordinary occurs in your life, someone or something worked awfully damn hard to make it happen — which is why we must always pay attention to them."

Rachel's take on this is the opposite: she believes every moment of life is a coincidence. It's all or nothing.

The teacher, however, also said, "The opposite of coincidence is entropy. Entropy is laziness. Entropy is energy being sucked away into nothingness. Entropy is the universe clocking fake hours on its time sheet. Entropy wants your car's tires to go flat; it wants your cake to fall; it wants your software to crash. It wants bad things for you. So remember, stay halfway between coincidence and entropy and you'll always be safe. Take my word for it, a day in which nothing bad happens is a miracle — it's a day in which all the things that could have gone wrong failed to go wrong. A dull day is a triumph of the human spirit; boredom is a luxury unprecedented in the history of our species."

That was when Rachel left her Happy Place and looked over at Warren's body. Karen was still screaming, but Luke kept her from leaving the truck. Rachel was trying to figure out if Warren's shooting was a coincidence or if there was cause and effect between his death and the fireball five kilometres away. Terrorists? Oil depot screw-up? Anarchists?

Rick, meanwhile, continued to yell to everyone to lie as low as possible, out of view of snipers. He said, "I'll start the truck and we'll boot directly out of here." But when he turned the key, the engine made a sickening I'm-not-going-to-start noise. "Oh God, Pam is right, I'm nothing but a goddam genetic dumpster. I *do* deserve everything that happens to me. I am a bad, bad person." He paused. "Does anyone else here have a car?"

No one did.

"What did Warren drive?"

Karen, through tears, said, "A truck, I think."

"What kind?"

"A *truck* truck. I don't know. They're all the same to me." Karen's voice had gone very high and pitchy.

Rachel said, "The only safe place to be is in the hotel. The lounge is too isolated. We have to run for cover."

Rick said, "I agree." The forcefulness of his words made Rachel wonder if Rick was an alpha male. Maybe he ought to be the one to father her first child. But there wouldn't be any child unless they ran to safety. Crawling out the passengerside doors, the group of four readied themselves to sprint hotelwards. Rick said, "One, two, three . . . go!"

They sprinted past Warren's corpse into the breezeway between the hotel and the lounge. They tried entering the main hotel building first, but on reaching its doors, they found them locked. They rattled the doors to little effect. They saw no people through the tinted glass.

Rick yelled, "Plan B — back into the lounge!"

Like flocking sparrows, they raced across the covered walkway to the lounge. Rick bolted the glass door and then he and Luke moved an ancient, dust-covered cigarette machine from a closet and pushed it in front of the door. On top of it they jammed a collection of folding tables and navy blue tablecloths. The door opened out, but anyone trying to get in would have a fairly substantial obstacle before him, and getting past it would slow down the intruder enough to give the group of four time to assume the best defensive positions.

Rachel peered into the closet where the cigarette machine had been stored. On the floor were spiders' nests and a clump of business cards so old they lacked area codes in front of the phone numbers. Even amidst the confusion, this absence of area codes struck Rachel as remarkable. Sometimes the events that mark the change from one era to another are so slow that they are invisible while they happen. At other times, like now, eras change within the seconds it takes words to scroll across the bottom of a TV screen.

Player One

This is Player One here with your story upgrade. I know that you, as this story's user, may be curious and wondering what are the next sequences to come, so I will not tease. What will happen next is that Karen's head will continue to spin, and as with Rachel, Karen's brain will make a duplicate copy of the afternoon's events. She will remember a game she played as a child, called Pretend You're Dead. She and her friends would run around, and someone would shout "Stop!" and they'd all drop to the ground. As quickly as possible, they had to shout out how they'd like to reincarnate, without overthinking their decisions. More often than not, they chose horses, cats, dogs, and colourful birds and insects. It will dawn on Karen, as she sits there behind the bar, in hiding from one or more snipers, that never once in all the times she played the game did anybody choose to come back as a human being. *Good decision*, she will think. *We are a wretched species, indeed.*

Rick will ask both himself and the cosmos, *Why is it that the only way we ever seem to take steps forward in life is through pain? Why is exposure to pain supposed to make us better people?* And the universe, like a cosmic high school principal speaking over a celestial PA system, will tell him, "Well, Richard, good things don't change people, and what is the point of doing anything if you're not going to change?"

Luke will feel as if time is moving in slow motion, and will reflect on the nature of time. If the day's events were a story, readers would have to wait for the next chapter to find out what happens next. When it comes to paintings, on the other hand, one glance is all you need to divine what will follow. Life is more like a book than a painting. Life makes you wait. Life forces everything into a sequence, time-coded by emotions and memories. Luke will decide that this is why people get mushy and think their lives have to be stories — to rationalize time's total domination over their lives.

So Luke will be sitting there in the bar wondering if the only reason time exists is so that emotions and dramas have an arena in which to play themselves out. What vanity to assume that an entire dimension exists solely to amuse human beings! Yet, to be practical, this theory *would* help explain the incredible advance planning and hard work the universe put into creating life — not just on earth but probably everywhere else, too — to allow emotions to rule the universe. Life can still have a purpose without God, he will think.

Oh! If only there were some way of leapfrogging dimensions so that I could take time and flatten it into a kind-of painting that made the past and the future instantly readable — how king-like that would be! But there's always a catch, Luke will think. *There'd always be some higher dimension that would prevent me from apprehending my own dimension fully. Nobody escapes. The only fact that makes our imprisonment within time*

bearable is that we're all trapped inside the cosmic cock-
tail lounge together.

Rachel will make a timeline in her head of all of
the events that have just occurred, and Rachel will
do this because she's good at sequencing — and that's
not just knowing pi to over a thousand digits. Sequencing events allows her to strip them of their ability to
frighten her. Sequencing events makes them safer. Her
grade ten English teacher once learned in the staff room
of Rachel's ability with pi and wondered if she could
sequence other things as well — so he asked Rachel to
write down everything that had happened in her day so
far, a keyboarded list that clocked in at fifty-five minutes and just over seven thousand words.

"You should write stories," he had suggested, but
Rachel told him stories were pointless. "Things go from
A to B to C," she said. "Calling it a story changes nothing.
It's just a sequence. That's all it is."

"What about the emotions stories stir up?" he protested.

"Sequences don't cause emotions."

"But they help us understand the universe — our
reason for living!"

"3.14159265358979932384626433 . . ."

Rachel couldn't read his facial expression, but she
did hear him sigh as he walked away to leave her in
peace. And as she catches a final glimpse of Warren's
corpse through a gap between the ancient cigarette
machine and the doorframe, Rachel will resume a

mantra she hasn't used in years, the mantra that goes *3.14159265358979932384626433* . . . And then, while mentally cycling through pi, she will look up at the ceiling, notice a ventilation shaft entrance, and then say to Rick, "Does that panel connect to a ventilation system that leads up to the roof?"

Rick will look up at a rectangular slot covered with a grille. "Yes," he will say, "it does."

God's Little Dumpsters

Karen

Karen and her three barmates are standing inside the door to the cocktail lounge, as a quartet, panting like dogs.

Luke asks, "How many other entrances are there into this place?"

"Just the rear delivery door," Rick says.

"Come on."

The two men race towards the rear door, with Rick hopping the bar to retrieve a shotgun from beneath the cash register.

Karen's brain's amygdala, like Rachel's, fortified by adrenaline, is now kicking in and is making a dual recording of current events — life now feels like it's happening in slow motion for genuine biological reasons.

Her BlackBerry rings — the outside world! It's Casey. "Mom?"

"Casey." Karen knows to downplay her situation. "Sweetie, are you okay?"

"I'm with Misha. We're outside the Husky station down at the crossroads. It's been one great big hockey riot for the past half-hour. There's no gas left. Everyone's going apeshit. I've been taking pictures."

"You're okay?"

"Of course I'm okay. I'll send you some photos after this. How did it go with Mr. Right?"

"It didn't work out too well. Casey . . ."

"Yeah?"

"I want you to go home. Okay, sweetie?"

"No way. There's too much action going on. It's crazy everywhere. It's kind of awesome."

"Casey, I don't care how awesome it is. I want you to go home, and once you get home I want you to phone the police and tell them to come immediately to the hotel lounge I'm at right now."

"Why? What's wrong?"

"Don't worry about me, Casey. Just do as I say. The phones aren't working properly here. I don't know how your call made it through. Go home. Call the police. Tell them to come here."

"Wait, Mom — aren't you flying back today?"

"I doubt it. I'm at the Airport Camelot Hotel."

"Mom, you're scaring me. Something's really wrong there. I can tell!"

"Don't be scared. But go home. Call the police."

"Mom?"

The phone dies and Karen stares at the garnish caddy filled with pineapple chunks, orange slices, and maraschino cherries. She remembers her college job waitressing. The bar's owner, Gordy, had told her that garnishes are the lungs of a restaurant, sucking up all the impurities and crap in the air and leaving the room fresher for everybody. "Karen, garnishes are God's little Dumpsters," Gordy had said. "So use the goddam cling wrap on them *now*." And that was how Karen became addicted to cling wrap, and that's why she finds herself cling-wrapping slightly dried-out beverage garnishes while thinking about riots, looting, no cars, no planes, and no food. She catches sight of herself in the mirror behind the liquor bottles. Her hair is a mess, as if she's groomed herself using only moistened fingertips. How rare it is that we catch glimpses of ourselves in mirrors — usually in public spaces — and see ourselves as strangers see us. Beneath the mirror sits a jar of beef jerky that looks like strips of sun-dried hobo. How can men eat that stuff?

From the computer across the room, Rachel says, "Oil is now technically $900 a barrel. But in reality, it's no longer for sale. And . . . and now my Internet connection has failed."

Karen yells, "Try the TV."

The beautiful but spooky Rachel goes to fiddle with the TV controls. Karen hears the two men dragging something heavy to block the rear door.

Karen says, "I'm going to make an inventory of all the food in this place."

Rachel, in her toneless white-mouse-breeding voice, replies, "Yes, a caloric assessment of our environment is a good idea."

A brief investigation reveals that the bar has no kitchen and that their larder consists of fruit wedges, beef jerky, and ten kilos of Cajun-flavoured bar snacks containing blanched peanuts, pretzels, sesame sticks, toasted corn, pepitas, chili bits, and soy nuts, or, as Karen views it with her new survivalist mindset, *Legumes, grains, seeds, and pods — ideal for life during wartime.*

She discovers a stack of new airtight Rubbermaid containers and begins distributing the food into them. She finds this task oddly soothing. It occurs to her that when you have one specific task at hand, the whole world looks completely different — more focused, somehow. Rinsing out a bowl, she thinks, *Most of us have only a dozen or so genuinely interesting moments in our lives; the rest is filler. Right now*, she thinks, *life feels like one of those real patches, with no additives or fillers or starch. My universe has become huge! The world is full of wonder and fear, and my life is a strand of magic moments strung together, a succession of mysteries revealed.* She feels as if she is in a trance.

Karen remembers another moment in her life that felt as big: when her husband proposed to her, saying: "A ring is a halo for your finger. From now on, we no longer cast two shadows, we cast one. You stole my loneliness. I don't want to lose you." While emptying out the bar-mix dregs from a white bulk bin, Karen reflects that falling out of love can happen as quickly as falling in, and that falling out of love is just as surely one of life's big moments.

Worry kicks in: *Will Casey go home? Will she reach the police? And if she does, are there enough police near the airport to provide safety to a world coping with no oil?*

There's a cracking noise outside the glass door. Karen and Rachel look up, then freeze. *Jesus Christ, the sniper's outside.* Karen walks to the door as though approaching, say, Madonna, at a restaurant — the reward might be great, or it could be a possibly fatal slap in the face. She peers over the cigarette machine through a slot in some smushed-up tablecloths and sees an old red car from the 1980s zoom past through the narrow walkway, barely missing Warren — poor, doomed Warren, marinating in a pool of his own blood on the other side of the barricaded glass door. Warren, part of a now long-gone world once fuelled by oil. *Sure, Warren looked like the kind of guy who spent weekends with a metal detector, combing beaches for lost wedding rings, but he didn't deserve — wait!* She emerges from her trance for a moment. *Somewhere outside is a freaking sniper!* She backs up quickly and looks at Rachel; the TV screen is out of view. She says, "Just a car going past. No idea who it was."

"Can you see any activity in the hotel?"

"Nothing."

Karen returns to her spot by the bar and chews on an orange slice. *Okay, Karen, very well. Your old life is gone now — no more sitting at the waiting room desk, watching destabilized souls come and go while you sit in an Aeron chair pushing electrons around with a stick. Your new life, barely ten minutes old, is dreamlike yet more real than real — like the vivid dreams you have in the morning just before waking up, the brain's richest sleep cycle. No more eight-hour days breathing office air that smells like five hundred sheets of twenty-pound bond paper roasting at a low temperature in a nearby oven. No more afternoons in which time feels stillborn. Work was never meant to be a person's whole life, so why do so many of us believe it is?*

Karen imagines the Safeway back home — probably already completely looted. And Casey? She'd be fine. And maybe the airport would open again soon. It had to. It might take a week, like after 9/11, but she would get home. She once heard that the best thing for the planet would be for everyone to stay in one place for five years: no more transience, no more geographical cures, no more petro-holidays. just a simple commitment to one spot.

Luke and Rick return from the back. "No one's getting in through that door," Rick says. "Not without a tank." He calls to Rachel. "Any news?"

"My guess is that oil is currently unavailable at any price. And I can't get the TV to work."

The men stand on either side of the front door, looking for any action outside. "Nothing," Luke says. "Just Warren."

Rick peeks out and says, "Hey, I see a jet that just took off — a jumbo. It's . . . Air France."

Rachel says, "I'm guessing it's that plane's last flight. It has to get home to its native hangar."

The men head to the bar, where Karen, in Mommode despite the seeming apocalypse, is pouring a bowl of bar mix for them. She asks Rick, "What's your guess — a solo sniper or one gun among many?"

"No idea," Rick says. "I'm trying to figure out in my head what direction the shots came from. As far as I can tell, right above us."

"Hey!" Luke interrupts. "Does that phone work?"

Everyone makes the connection at once: *a land-line*. Karen reaches for it, hears a dial tone, and dials 911. The sound from the receiver is loud. The phone clicks, dials, clicks again, and then plays, of all things, an automated hurricane warning. "No surprise there. Any of you have kids?"

Rick says, "A boy. Tyler. School's out for the day. He may be home now." He pauses.

"Okay," Karen says, "while we try to figure out some other way of getting help, I'm having a drink. Who else wants one?"

———

The quartet sat on the floor behind the bar with their drinks, positioned halfway between the exits — the safest location, given all options. There was some discussion about the chaos that would surely ensue in the outside world, echoes of the 1973 oil shock but infinitely worse: the only gas people were going to get was whatever they still had in their tanks, maybe enough to get to work a few more times — except work was probably gone now too. Kill your neighbour for a tank? Why not? Will the military help out? Oh, *please*. Karen remembered a few months back seeing a truck that looked military, but she wasn't sure if it was real or from a film shoot.

Society was frozen, with no means of thawing out. No more cheap, easy food, no more travel, and, most likely, no more middle class.

Karen got a sad vibe from Luke as he thought about society's cookie crumbling; from Rachel, she perceived no emotion.

There was a silent patch, then Rachel said, "Growing up, I had to take courses on how to live with normal people."

"What do you mean?" asked Karen, curious to finally learn something about the woman in the $3,000 Chanel dress, or a very good copy of one.

"How to interpret the noises you make and the things you do. Like laughing. Medically, clinically, I have no sense of humour. A lesion in my brain's right hemisphere creates tone-blindness that hinders my ability to appreciate what you call humour, irony, passion, and God. Another right-hemisphere lesion strips my speech of inflection and tone. People say I sound like a robot. I can't tell. And finally, I have autism-related facial recognition blindness syndrome. Which is all to say that when people make the laughing noise, I have to talk myself out of being frightened."

"Is there a name for your condition?"

"I have several. I have autistic spectrum disorder. I have problems with inhibition and disinhibition, as well as mild OCD. My sequencing abilities are in the top half percentile. I know pi to just over one thousand digits."

"I've seen a few people with that come through the office I work in — *used to* work in. So you can't tell faces apart?"

"No."

"Can you tell if loud people are angry or happy?"

"A little bit. But in normalcy training I learned a set of questions one can ask to neutralize emotionally extreme situations, such as right now."

"Like what?"

"For example, you can always ask neurotypical people what their job is, and what they've learned through their jobs. And, as I believe we need a distraction here, I'm going to initiate this procedure. Luke, you have a wad of cash in your pocket and recently lost your religious faith. Can you tell us more about what you do?"

Luke waited for Karen to hand him his drink before saying, "Up until this morning I was a pastor in a nice little church beside a freeway off-ramp up in Nippissing. But yesterday I lost my faith, and this morning I stole the church's entire renovation fund, jumped on a plane, and came here."

"Seriously?" asked Rick.

"Yup. Twenty grand." Luke sipped his Scotch.

"So," said Rachel, "technically you're unemployed?"

"Yup."

"Can you tell us anything you've learned about people from your job as a small-town pastor?"

A funny expression crossed Luke's face — a combination of amusement and relief. "It seems like I've been waiting over a decade for someone to ask me that very question." Luke paused for a moment, as if ordering his thoughts, then said, "Here goes. To start with, if you're at work and someone's bothering you, ask him or her to make a donation to a charity. Keep a charity can and donation envelopes in your desk. They'll never bug you again. It works."

"What else?"

"What else? Okay, chances are you feel superior to almost everyone you work with — but they probably feel the same way about you. Also, more men than you might think beat their wives with full plastic bottles of fabric softener." Luke stared at the ceiling as he continued his litany. "Relentlessly perky women often have deeply rooted fertility issues. Also, for the first time in history, thanks to the Internet, straight people are having way more sex than gay people. And I think I can easily generalize and say that too much free time is a monkey's paw in disguise. Humans weren't built to handle a structureless life."

Rachel asked, "What else?"

"What else . . . Here's one: by the age of twenty, you know you're not going to be a rock star. By twenty-five,

you know you're not going to be a dentist or any kind
of professional. And by thirty, darkness starts moving
in — you wonder if you're ever going to be fulfilled, let
alone wealthy or successful. By thirty-five, you know,
basically, what you're going to be doing for the rest of
your life, and you become resigned to your fate."

Luke paused and rubbed a finger around the rim of
his glass. "You know, in the end I just got so darned tired
of hearing about the same old seven sins over and over
again. You might think it would be interesting, but it's
not. Would someone please invent an eighth sin to keep
things lively?"

Karen resisted her impulse to interrupt.

Luke continued, "I mean, why do people live so long?
What could be the difference between death at fifty-five
and death at sixty-five or seventy-five or eighty-five?
Those extra years . . . what benefit could they possibly
have? Why do we go on living even though nothing new
happens, nothing new is learned, and nothing new is
transmitted? At fifty-five, your story's pretty much over."

Luke polished off his drink. "You know, I think the
people I feel saddest for are the ones who once knew
what profoundness was, but who lost or became numb
to the sensation of wonder, who felt their emotions
floating away and just didn't care. I guess that's what's
scariest: not caring about the loss."

Rachel said, "So you feel sad for, and frightened by,
yourself."

"Yes."

There was a silence, then Rachel asked, "Rick, what have you learned from your job?"

"I've learned that I'm often my own worst enemy. I've learned that I'd rather be in pain than be wrong. I've learned that sometimes failure isn't an opportunity in disguise: it's just me. I've learned that I'll never be rich, because I don't like rich people. I've learned that you can be a total shithead, and yet your soul will still want to hang out with you. Souls ought to have some kind of legal right to bail once you cross certain behaviour thresholds."

"Anything else you've learned from work specifically?" asks Rachel.

"I won't go too much into my work history, except to say that I was actually making an okay go of my gardening business until someone who doesn't deserve their soul swiped my truck and all my equipment, and that's how I ended up working in this bar, hearing the same things you heard from your parishioners, Luke — except I probably get the opposite end of the bullshit spectrum: the wishful thinking and the grandiosity people launch into by beer number three. Do people — *did* people — ever tell you the good stuff? Or did they just dump on you with all their crap and baggage?"

"Just the crap. I think maybe I should have been a bartender."

"You're missing nothing. Aim low, brother. Sell roadside corn. There's a lot to be said for having a small, manageable dream." Rick looked at Karen. "What about you?"

"Me? I don't know. Maybe I didn't learn much. I work as a receptionist for three psychiatrists. I see a lot of crazy. But I think crazy people — okay, not crazy, but people at the extremes of normal behaviour — are more interesting than so-called normal people. I've learned that one of the biggest indicators for success in life is having a few crazy relatives. So long as you get only some of the crazy genes, you don't end up crazy; you merely end up different. And it's that difference that gives you an edge, that makes you successful."

"I've never thought of it that way," said Luke.

"I've also learned that if you're on meds, it's much better to stick to them. I mean, would you rather jump off a bridge because you couldn't be bothered to take one lousy pill? Also, when agitated patients come in, I tell them some kind of story about my cat, Rusty. Listening to people tell stories is very soothing. When someone is telling you a story, they hijack the personal narrator that lives inside your head. It's the closest we come to seeing through someone else's eyes."

Rick

In his early twenties, Rick worked at a Texaco gas station, and when he was pumping gas, he liked to watch the numbers rev higher and higher on the pumps. He pretended these speedily increasing numbers didn't represent money at all; rather, one penny equalled one year. He watched Western history begin at Year Zero-Zero-Zero-One and clip upwards and upwards: the Dark Ages . . . the Renaissance . . . 1776 . . . railways . . . the Panama Canal . . . the Great Depression . . . World War II . . . suburbia . . . JFK . . . Vietnam . . . disco . . . Mount St. Helens . . . 1984 . . . grunge . . . until, *WHAM!*, he'd hit the wall of the present with the death of Kurt Cobain. Whenever Rick did this mental exercise, there was a magic little piece of time a few numbers past $19.94 when he felt as if he were in the future.

And that's how he feels standing inside the lounge after barricading the front door against the outside world. Except now there's no other time stream to slip back into; he's now living in the future 24/7. He rubs a cut on his left index finger, incurred while moving the ancient cigarette machine, its faded, yellowing image of Niagara Falls making it look older than a relic from King Tut's tomb. He already knows he's going to miss the past a lot. He hops the bar and scoops up the Winchester Model 12 shotgun stashed beneath the cash register, then follows Luke to the rear exit, where he and Luke use a dolly to jimmy the hulking ice machine in front of the locked door.

Rick doesn't know what to make of the trio he's been billeted with by the gods. As far as he can see, Luke is a disastrous drunk and possibly a scammer, Karen is a soccer mom going wrong, and Rachel is from another planet. But he doesn't spend too much time thinking about them. He's busy scanning the back area, looking for something, anything, he could use to kill a human being. But there's precious little to weaponize, save for broken bottles and some cutlery. Thankfully, he has the shotgun his ex told him he was crazy to keep on the premises. She'd stopped by with Tyler a year or so ago, taken a look around the place, and said it was like a crack den without the crack. "And what's with the stretch-waist rugby pants you're wearing, Rick? Jesus, you look like a 1982 liquor store clerk with herpes." Tyler was cleaning out the dish of bar mix, and Pam slapped his fingers away, saying, "Jesus, Tyler, they'll put anything in that stuff." She looked at Rick. "So let me get this straight — you want to keep a *shotgun* around so you can shoot somebody over something stupid like a hundred bucks from the till?"

Who's got the last laugh now?

Rick thinks, *Right now is the end of some aspect of my life, but it's also a beginning — the beginning of some unknown secret that will reveal itself to me soon.*

Rick thinks, *Nothing very, very good and nothing very, very bad ever lasts for very, very long.*

Rick thinks, *My head feels like Niagara Falls without the noise, just this mist and this churning and no real sense of where the earth ends and the heavens begin.*

Rick wants a drink.

Rick wants a great big crowbar to crack him open so he can take whatever creature is sitting inside him and shake it clean like a rug, then rinse it in a cold, clear lake, and then put it under the sun to heal and dry and grow and come to consciousness again with a clear and quiet mind.

And then suddenly he's sitting with three semi-strangers on the ceramic tiles behind the bar, getting at least one of his wishes granted: a double vodka and soda with a lemon twist. Guilt be damned! Rick knows that alcohol will initially enhance his experience of events as they take place, even though in the end it will scramble his recall of the present tense, like sprinkling MSG into the soup tureen of his consciousness and waiting for the time headache to begin.

The group has been discussing what they've learned from their jobs — not something Rick might expect in a situation like this, but the unexpectedness of the topic feels intense and correct. Karen has just finished and it's Rachel's turn, but before she begins she asks, "Rick, what is the killing capacity of your shotgun?"

"This puppy? Five shots in the chamber, double-ought buck — pretty much all you need for human beings."

"Are you skilled at using it?"

"I am." Rick thinks, *This robot woman is hot.*

But robot woman has Rick nailed. "That's good, Rick. Please, may I ask you to limit the number of cocktails you drink over the next few hours? Marksmanship may become a life-or-death skill the four of us will require."

Rachel then starts to tell them what she has learned from her job breeding white mice. "To begin with, I suggest raising as few male mice as possible, as they secrete a glandular odour that is hard to get used to, even after months of daily exposure."

Oh dear God, Rick thinks. *I suppose white mice have to come from somewhere. Costa Rica? West Virginia? But from Rachel's garage? That's a lot to absorb. And how did she know about me and my booze jones? Forget about it. What else can I use in this heinous dump to kill people?* Rick scours the bar area, looking for items he can weaponize: an unopened Coca-Cola syrup canister heated on the coffee burner until hot and then shot with the Model 12 would make an excellent bomb; any pen or pencil can be rammed into the jugular à la Joe Pesci; a sniper's head could be wrapped in a white tablecloth and then pushed underwater in a grey plastic busing tray.

Rachel is still talking about white mice. Rick realizes he is a little bit drunk after blowing fourteen months of sobriety. Rachel says it is fairly easy to assess a mouse's needs, and Rick finds himself saying, "I agree." The others stare at him, and he continues, "But people are different from mice. Never let *anyone* assess what you want or need out of life. You might as well send them engraved invitations saying, 'Hi, this is what I want you to prevent me from having.' Life always kills you in the end, but first it stops you from getting what you want. I'm so tired of never getting what I want. Or of getting it with a monkey's-paw curse attached."

If being interrupted annoys Rachel, her face shows no sign of it.

"I'm not bitter," Rick adds. "But what if I was? At least you'd know where I stand."

Somewhere in the distance something explodes. The conversation stops and everyone cocks their ears.

Luke looks at Rick and says, "The heart of a man is like deep water."

"I'm no better than my father," Rick says. "He's in Saskatchewan. His liver has gone all marshmallowy. He should have been dead ten years ago. But instead he started taking 2,000 IUs of vitamin D a day, so now he's got an immune system like a pit bull's rubber chew toy."

"My father is an alcoholic," Rachel says. "And he doesn't think I'm a true human being, so I'm going to surprise him by reproducing. Then he can't say I'm not human anymore."

The group stares at her. To Rick she says, "Please don't drink anything more today. For my sake."

Rick looks at Rachel, thinks it over, then puts down his drink. He never realized it could be this easy.

———

There was another explosion, closer this time. "It's not just that there's no jet noise," Luke said. "There are no sirens either. It's as if it's not just cars and planes and helicopters that have stopped — it's like *time* has stopped."

Karen said, "You'd think by now there'd be a SWAT team here. Not to mention the Navy SEALs, James Bond, and Charlie's Angels."

Rachel was looking at Rick with an intensity he found sexy and hadn't thought she was capable of. Rick, meanwhile, had toppled the first domino in the cascade of falling in love. He had once seen a TV game show that asked how many times the average person falls in love. The answer was six. Since then, Rick had come to believe that people are able to fall in love only six times in their life. According to this rule, Rick was left with just one more love — he'd burnt through five already, three of them before he turned twenty-two — and now here was the moment when the hammer strikes the anvil and the chain is forged and the love grows strong, becomes real, becomes permanent. Rick *wanted* to fall in love again — even more than he wanted to reinvent himself via the Power Dynamics Seminar System — but what if this last love didn't work out? Then he'd be lonely for the rest of his life, or worse, he'd have to find some newer, more extreme experience than love, whatever that might be. Nevertheless, sitting there on the ceramic floor, he wondered, *Does Rachel feel anything for me? How can I make her feel something for me, this woman who has no anatomical capacity to experience emotion? I bet I could get through to her. I bet I could make her understand what it means to be in love.* "Rachel, can I get you a drink?"

"Please. A ginger ale."

"Coming right up."

Karen said, "Guys, what exactly are we going to do here? Just wait? For what — to get shot, like Warren?"

Luke said, "I think maybe that's all we *can* do." He had found the banker's box that served as the bar's lost and found. There were three cellphones in it. He tried all three for dial tones and got one. "Rick, buddy, you take it. Call your kid."

Rick handed Rachel her ginger ale and took the phone from Luke. But before he could dial, Karen's phone rang. "Casey?"

"Mom, they set fire to the outlet mall! You can probably see the smoke from outer space. It's anarchy here."

"Casey, are you at home now?"

"I am. But I wish I was out there, looking at all the craziness."

"Did you get through to the police?"

"I'm trying. The phones are all screwed."

"Casey, stay home. I don't want you going anywhere. Can you get hold of your father?"

"I can't get through to him."

The connection died.

Rick tried to reach his son but couldn't get a dial tone on either Karen's BlackBerry or the phone from the lost and found. The four sat in silence.

Luke

Three years ago, Luke's father's early-onset Alzheimer's became so relentless that he could no longer live at home — his unforgiving father, who had once said to Luke while they were walking along a beach, "I don't cast a shadow, son, I cast *light*"; his firm, unforgiving father, Caleb, who had once told Luke that the opposite of labour is not leisure but theft.

Caleb had always treated Luke as if there was no doubt he would follow in his footsteps, yet at the same time Caleb made it consistently clear that Luke would never be as spiritual as himself. Like most father/son ego battles, the going could be both nasty and pathetic. Several times Caleb entered Luke's bedroom when Luke was nine and caught him playing with plastic soldiers. He fetched the cordless phone, brought it into the bedroom, sat down on the bed, and said, "Fine, have your soldiers kill each other, but every time one of them dies, I am going to sit here and telephone his mother."

"Father, they're plastic soldiers."

"To you, but not to the *better part* of you."

"Okay. Call their mothers."

"Okay, I will. That one toppled over there . . ." Luke's father dialled seven numbers, and even though Luke could hear a busy signal, his father said, "Hello, Mrs. Miller. This is Pastor French calling. I'm afraid I have terrible news for you, Mrs. Miller: your son is dead. No, there's no mistake. He was shot today in a battle. What battle? I don't know. You'd have to speak to the person I once thought was my son to find out what sort of battle. I'm sorry, Mrs. Miller. Mrs. Miller, stop your screaming and crying. Yes, I'm absolutely sure he's dead. Yes. And my son is the killer."

The battle never did end, not until the Alzheimer's struck, and struck swiftly. Luke's overwhelmed mother managed to locate a care facility on the west coast that specialized in patients whose lives had been spent in the ministry. She'd been driving Caleb across the country when an avalanche from a British Columbia mountainside swallowed their car and a dozen others, covering them with so much rock and soil that excavation was impossible. Since then, Luke has had to live with the knowledge that those meat-covered skeletons resting inside their Volkswagens or Cutlasses or camper vans are still there, and will still be there, exactly where they are right now, trapped forever inside the mountain, until the sun goes supernova in a billion years or so. Those bodies bind us to the future. They're time-frozen. Tomorrow = yesterday = today = the same thing, always.

And their entombment is different from being buried in a graveyard. Six feet of dirt is nothing. In a hundred years, raiding the graves of our current era will be an excellent source of income for the unscrupulous. But to be *inside a mountain* — that messes with Luke's mind. When does time end? When do people end? On his flight into Toronto this morning, Luke thought about time and evolution. *Let's think long term, Luke. What are we evolving* towards? *Do we just go along, day by day, drinking coffee, building golf courses, making photocopies, and having wars until we all mutate and turn into a new species? How long are we supposed to keep on doing all this stuff we do? If we don't mutate quickly, in ten thousand years we're merely going to be the same humans we are now, except we'll have run out of resources. Will the planet's population ever decrease? It will have to, if not simply because our sun will go supernova. So where, between now and the sun going supernova in a billion years, does society end? When do people end? When does the population start to shrink? It's a mathematical certainty. So then when? When? When?*

Even with his faith recently nullified, Luke believes in sin. He believes that what separates humanity from everything else in this world — spaghetti, binder paper, deep-sea creatures, edelweiss, and Mount McKinley — is that humanity alone has the capacity, at any given moment, to commit all possible sins. Even those of us who try to live a good and true life remain as far away from grace as the Hillside Strangler or any demon who ever tried to poison the village well.

In Luke's eyes, sin defines our lives in ways both pathetic and monstrous. And Luke knows that monsters exist: entities with human forms but no souls. Ronnie, who set fire to his house with his two children inside. Lacey, who extinguished cigarettes on her baby's arms. In the face of monsters, a mere seven deadly sins seems almost charming, and certainly out of touch with the twenty-first century. Luke thinks sins badly need updating, and he keeps a running list in his head of contemporary sins that religions might well consider: the willingness to tolerate information overload; the neglect of the maintenance of democracy; the deliberate ignorance of history; the equating of shopping with creativity; the rejection of reflective thinking; the belief that spectacle is reality; vicarious living through celebrities. And more, so much more.

Man, Luke thinks, *I am one judgemental prick. I'm turning into my father — I have to try harder to be different. Losing faith wasn't enough.* But, of course, Luke has also learned from his flock that the harder one tries to be different from one's parents, the more quickly one becomes them.

Luke notices that Rick has his eyes set on Rachel, and Rachel seems to have hers set on Rick. Luke's embezzled twenty grand is most likely worthless in a post-oil economy, so his Darwinian advantage over Rick is gone. But Luke's need to stay alive overpowers all, even his need to reproduce. And before long, Luke finds himself looking up at Rick, who's standing on the bar, prying a ventilation grille off the ceiling. The plan is for Rick and Luke to crawl up into the ventilation system and try to find grilles or faceplates they can pop out so they can scan the area around the building, locate the sniper or snipers, if possible, and find a safe way out of the situation.

The ceiling grille comes off with a dry hiss reminiscent of soil being tossed onto a coffin. Rick stores it above the ceiling, inside the crawl area, and looks inside. "Holy crap. There's a ton of space up here. Seriously. It's huge."

Karen says, "Keep your voice down." Karen and Rachel are still on the floor behind the bar.

"I'm going in. Hand me the shotgun once I'm up there."

"Be careful with that thing!" Karen says.

Rick lifts himself up inside the crawl space. Luke passes him the shotgun, then joins him. It's dark but not black inside. Roasting hot sunlight seeps in through vent holes on both sides, as well as from various tubes and shafts connecting the roof to the building's guts.

Luke says, "Shh . . ." and puts his finger to his lips. "Do you hear that?"

The men fall silent. Above them, over towards the east side of the roof, they hear footsteps crunching on the gravel.

Luke says, "It's him."

———

Luke and Rick crept through the crawl space until an opening appeared in the ceiling. Rick peered up, then gave Luke the okay sign and quietly pulled himself up into a slatted ventilator housing. Luke quickly followed. Through the slats, they could see the sniper. He was standing at hyper-attention by the knee-high wall that encircled the roof of the cocktail lounge. He resembled a high school chemistry teacher — certainly no swarthy terrorist cliché. A black beard, beige slacks, a dark blue James Dean zip-up jacket, a black baseball cap, plus repeat-sex-offender eyeglasses like those of his murder victim Warren. *Wait*, Luke realized, *he's wearing Warren's actual glasses. This guy is a trophy taker.*

"One guy?" Rick whispered.

"What the hell is he doing on the roof? And how did he get up there?"

Rick said, "I'm going to take him out," and Luke said, "Do it," then stopped Rick. "Wait. Are we sure this guy's alone?"

The two men scoped the 360 degrees around the housing. To the south, huge fires burned at the source of the explosions. As Rick and Luke watched, there was another explosion, accompanied by a glowing mushroom-shaped cloud rich with turquoise highlights. But as for people, they saw nobody, and the monster's body language gave no indication that he was communicating with anyone. For the most part, his attention was focused on the fifteen-storey hotel block across the breezeway from the bar. It was hard to imagine anyone at the hotel being stupid enough to be standing by its windows. They could hear a few sirens, but far away, and there was a fraction of the normal traffic noise. The world had gone mute.

Despite the dusty enclosure's roasting heat, Luke felt chilled as he watched the monster, who was standing straight, ears cocked, waiting to kill. It reminded him of the time he had food poisoning in California and thought he was boiling to death and freezing to death at the same time. Outwardly, the monster seemed so harmless — that's what scared Luke the most. Still waters truly do run deepest.

Luke said, "Let's not make any noise and screw this up. Jesus, look at that chemical cloud coming in." A peanut-shaped cloud the size of a weather system was drifting towards the building, but its impending arrival didn't alter the monster's behaviour. He walked efficiently back and forth along the lounge's eastern lip, scouting out new targets, unfazed by any possibility of retaliation. He heard something below, out in front of the hotel. With hawk-like speed, he raised his rifle and took three shots. Luke and Rick heard a woman scream, and then there was silence. The monster knelt on the gravel, concealed by the roof's lip, and reloaded a 6.5-millimetre Italian carbine with a four-power scope, identical to the one used by Lee Harvey Oswald to kill John F. Kennedy in 1963. Rick recognized it and told Luke what it was, adding, "This guy's good. This guy knows his history."

"That's very comforting, Rick."

"I'm just saying this guy is a player."

"So shoot him already."

Rick tried manoeuvring the shotgun into a position from which he could aim and fire, but the shape of the vent made it impossible. Luke looked across the roof to a larger vent. "We have to go over there."

So the two men went back down to the crawl space and crept towards the other side of the roof. They heard the monster's crunching steps above them. He would walk, stop, continue walking, then stop again. When they reached their destination, Luke said, "There's no way he knows we're here. I think we can nail the bastard from in there."

They pulled up into a newer, larger ventilation structure. *Bingo.*

Rick whispered, "I think we can do this."

Luke said, "Come on, come on, be done with it," and realized that, in his impatience, he sounded like Caleb. And then, in the midst of all the craziness, Luke found himself thinking about families. *In the end, every family experiences an equal amount of trials, conditions, quirks, and medical dilemmas. One family might get more cancer, another more bipolar or schizo, but in the end it all averages out. It's a testament to the ambivalence most people feel about their families that they don't care to know more of their family history than the past three generations. There are so many reasons for not wanting to know.* Caleb had once said, "Be as pious as you want; people are slime." Luke himself would say, "We're all slime in the eyes of God."

Luke snapped back to the present moment. "Get on with it," he hissed. "Shoot."

"Right."

Rick had his finger on the trigger when another chemical explosion startled him and the shotgun's barrel clanked against an aluminum slat. The monster swivelled. Rick fired and missed, and he and Luke saw the monster raise his rifle and aim it at the ventilation housing.

"Jesus, let's get out of here!"

The two men dropped back into the crawl area and raced to the opening above the bar. Rick shouted, "Catch!" and dropped the shotgun down to Rachel. Within seconds, both men had scrambled back into the lounge.

Karen demanded, "What happened?"

"It's one guy," said Luke. "He's armed to the teeth."

"Is he coming down through the roof?" Rachel asked.

"No. He's not stupid. If he did, we'd have a massive tactical advantage."

Karen asked, "What's he doing on our roof? Why isn't he picking off people at the airport or some place with more people?"

Rachel asked, "Did he appear to have any sort of focus — was he scanning any particular area?"

"Yes," said Luke. "The front door of the hotel. He didn't even care about those chemical explosions upwind."

Rick added, "I'll go turn off all the fans. You can't believe how much fallout there is out there. And it's all headed this way."

Rachel

Rachel is feeling slightly guilty because when she was at the computer, supposedly looking up the price of oil, she was actually visiting a white mouse-breeding website to see if the day's events had altered the price of mice. It hadn't changed, but then the site staff is always so slow to update. Just before the computer crashed, she caught the $900 sweet crude oil price on the Drudge Report.

The bar's TV set is also no help, and Rachel feels as if she isn't contributing to collective safety the way the others are doing. Karen is inventorying food. The men are safeguarding the lounge's rear entrance. Rachel feels like the female character on a TV outer space drama who sits at the control deck doing little but repeating things the captain has already said — and that's the *last* character she wants to be. Whenever the subject of TV came up during lemonade-and-cookie time at normalcy training, Rachel and her classmates agreed that they wanted to be aliens, not humans, as long as they *weren't* the emotionless Spock aliens, because that was what everyone expected them to be. Rachel is neither an alien nor a robot, and she does, indeed, experience emotions — even if the emotions are usually variations of confusion. But she knows there are many things her brain simply isn't wired to "get." The list includes humour, beauty, voice inflection, musicality, irony, sarcasm, and metaphor. Metaphor! How is a burning book supposed to represent Hitler? Or fascism! A book is a book. Hitler is Hitler. Why do fields of daisies in soft focus equal love? They're plants! Not love!

Love.

Well, at least Rachel gets love. Or she thinks she gets it — she hopes she gets it, because it's all that neurotypical people ever seem to talk about or sing songs about. She does feel strongly about a few things, and she hopes this is love. She loves the first thirty seconds of "A Rush and a Push and the Land Is Ours" by the Smiths — the song's noises that, in a way that defies verb tenses, remind her of what it feels like to be a ghost. Rachel also loves the sight of pigeons huddled for the night below the downtown bridges. She loves the first snowfall of the year, and she loves grilled cheese sandwiches with double ketchup, as long as the ketchup is on the side and in no way touches her sandwich until she elects to dip it. She loves her mice and her parents and Mrs. Hovell at the training centre. And she especially likes her Second Life avatar — her fearless disembodied electronic double who ventures into all rooms and spaces, who doesn't have to experience such mundane problems as muggy weather and unexpected noises, who doesn't need to eat the disgusting-textured salty-sugary-greasy, always unpredictable stuff that normal people call "food." Her avatar is free, and her only goal is to roam the universe pursuing truth and victory. Her avatar has emotions; she simply chooses not to use them.

When the men finish barricading the rear door and they all wind up sitting behind the bar, the others seem stressed and frightened. Rachel has learned to recognize people's states of mind from their body language, since she can't read facial expressions. Rachel is neither stressed nor frightened; she believes adequate measures have been taken to ensure their collective safety. But she has an idea that might help cut the tension. Mrs. Hovell once told her, "Rachel, if you're ever in a real fix and need something to discuss, ask people what their jobs are and what they have learned from them." Mrs. Hovell is full of good advice. Another piece that always works for Rachel is this: Whenever you encounter a person who appears exhausted and stressed, tell them, "You look really great. You look really relaxed. I wish I had what you have." It immediately relaxes them.

So Rachel brings up the subject of jobs, and (thank you, Mrs. Hovell) the question works — everyone is distracted for a little while. As she is telling the group about her mouse-breeding business, Rick interrupts her with a series of statements she knows are gloomy. Rachel has trained herself not to respond to interruptions. But of pivotal importance is the fact that Rick, with his nihilistic outbursts, very much resembles her father — and therefore *he* should ultimately be the man to sire her child. The only problem is that Rick's face lacks distinguishing characteristics and is difficult to memorize. Rachel stares at him, trying extra hard to find anomalies that would make it easier for her to pick him out of a crowd if he were to wear clothing other than a bartender's black pants and white shirt. Is that a mole? No. A scar? No. At least Leslie Freemont, with his white mane, was highly recognizable. He also had a mole on his left cheek, an asymmetrical mouth, and almost triangular spatulate fingernails — but the hair made those details unnecessary. Happily, Rick is also looking closely at Rachel. Most people don't like being studied this way. Rachel wonders if Rick's willingness to be studied will make him an even better father. As a bonus, he offers to get her a ginger ale at the very moment when she feels in need of a beverage. He is what her mother would call a gentleman. Except, her mother's opinion doesn't matter to her; only her father's opinion counts.

This is when Karen's daughter phones with her news about the new world without oil — a world that possibly has no need for expertly bred white mice. Rachel tries not to listen in on the conversation and starts looking around, analyzing the room around her. She tries to determine if the bar's designer consciously set out to create an environment that fosters zero-commitment sexual hookups. While taking the bus to the lounge that morning, she had thought the bar would be covered with sparkly surfaces, and the music in the background would sound beepy, like Super Mario video games. Instead she looks around her and sees low-wattage lighting, no bright colours save for the icky red vinyl wall by the computer, and a collection of fabric-covered stools that don't seem to have been properly cleaned and are most likely brimming with decades' worth of bum molecules. Finally, she looks up at the ceiling, which is when she notices a ventilation shaft entrance.

Once the men have gone up into the crawl space, Karen and Rachel resume their positions on the floor behind the bar. Karen's arms are crossed, a sign of worry. Rachel says, "Karen, you look really great. You look really relaxed. I wish I had what you have."

Karen pats her hair and says, "Really?"

Rachel says, "Yes."

Karen says, "Because obviously there's been so much confusion. I thought my look had come slightly apart."

Rachel says, "No, you look terrific. Karen, I have a question for you."

"Shoot."

"I've decided to make Rick the father of my child. What do you think of this decision?"

Karen pauses, is about to say something, pauses again, and then says, "Well, I hope you have a steady income stream of your own. Can white mice do that for you?"

"Yes, I believe society will continue to need white mice, even a society permanently crippled by diminished oil and all of the political, economical, and environmental anarchy the shortage has already begun to unleash."

Karen asks, "Rachel, are you human?"

Rachel replies, "I've been asked that question many times. I know it is meant humorously and I don't take offence at it."

"I was just —"

"That's okay, don't worry. I personally worry that maybe I'm nothing more than my medical condition. If I didn't have my brain anomalies, which others seem to perceive as damage, maybe I'd be a normal person instead — whatever I was actually *meant* to be like, something better than just a broken woman. If I was normal, I wouldn't have to go to normalcy training lessons — and my father wouldn't be ashamed to tell his work friends that I've entered the Fifty Thousand Mouse Club."

"Rachel, I work in a psychiatrist's office. I see people all day, in and out of their conditions. Who they are at any given time is usually based on whether they're sticking to their meds."

"What is your conclusion? Are these people really people? Or are they only their conditions?"

"I think we're everything: our brain's wiring, the things our mothers ate when they were pregnant, the TV show we watched last night, the friend who betrayed us in grade ten, the way our parents punished us. These days we have PET scans, MRIs, gene mapping, and massive research into psychopharmacology — so many ways of explaining the human condition. Personality is more like a . . . a potato salad composed of your history plus all of your body's quirks, good and bad. Tell me, Rachel, and be honest: if you could take a pill and be 'normal,' would you?"

Rachel thinks about what Karen has said. After an uncomfortably long time, she says, "*Potato salad?*"

And that's when Rick shouts, "Catch!" and drops his shotgun down into the lounge.

———

Things happened quickly, yet in slow motion. Rick raced to shut off the ventilation system, while Rachel, Karen, and Luke went to the front door to look for ways to further block it. Looking outside, they saw a chemical blizzard — it was like watching the World Trade Center collapse, but with coloured dust, not just grey, and with what resembled fragments of hornets' nests drifting and landing higgledy-piggledy in all directions. Daylight had vanished. The red carpet that led along the covered walkway to the hotel was inch-deep in crud, as was the body of the unfortunate Warren.

Karen asked, "What the hell is that stuff?"

Luke shouted for her to get away from the glass. "He's off the roof and he's coming this way."

From the left, a stone's throw away, came the sniper, his face curled into his chest. He lurched towards the lounge, a duffle bag slung over one shoulder, his other arm trying to protect his face from the toxic blizzard but still holding a rifle.

"Karen, get Rick's gun! Get it now! Rachel, help me put these stacking chairs in front of the door. If he reaches for his rifle, run like hell."

Rachel worked fast to further barricade the door, inserting heavy steel stacking chairs into whatever slots she could. They heard the sniper trying to open car doors outside the hotel. Through a slit in the fabric of one of the tablecloths, Rachel saw the sniper curse, particles getting stuck in his mouth as he did. Most of his concentration and energy was going into trying to breathe and cover his eyes at the same time. Rachel saw two dead pigeons fall onto the dust-covered pavement, and she knew it would only get worse. And then it did. The sniper looked up, seemed to realize there were people behind the barricaded door, and raced towards them.

Rachel wasn't frightened, nor was she confused. She walked away from the door and said, "He's here. Is the shotgun ready?"

Rick ran in from the back and grabbed his weapon from Karen. "Where is he?"

"Outside the door."

"Crap."

They heard shattering glass and the sound of feet kicking at something. The sniper's voice called, "Get this machine out of the way!"

Rick peeked around the corner: The sniper was trying to get in — as were the toxic cloud chemicals. The sniper said, "It's either let me in or we all die from this crap that's blowing around. Choose your fate. I promise I won't shoot if you let me in, but I sure as hell will if you try to seal this door against the chemicals without letting me in."

Rick shouted out, "Throw your rifle inside."

There was silence.

"I said, throw your rifle inside or *we* shoot *you*."

More silence.

"Okay, then, hellfire it is for you."

They heard some stacking chairs topple to the ground, then the Italian rifle was tossed into the lounge.

"Okay," said Luke, picking up the rifle. "Let him in and let's seal up that door. I can't even see Warren through all that chemical shit out there."

As Luke covered the door with the rifle, Rachel and Karen opened a slot in the clutter barrier just big enough for the sniper to enter the lounge. Once he was past them and moving towards the bar, arms up and the canvas duffle bag in his left hand, Rick took over covering him with the shotgun while Luke, Rachel, and Karen worked together to barricade and seal the door. Karen had found a roll of duct tape in the closet and immediately started taping tablecloths to the door frame.

"What's in the bag?" asked Rick.

"Nothing. Check for yourself." The sniper set the bag on the bar.

Rick inspected the bag and found only shell casings and some bloody rags. The sniper went behind the bar and rinsed his face under the tap. Rick stood guard while the others finished sealing the door, using garments from the lost and found and a black plastic signboard with its few remaining white plastic letters spelling ROTARIAN SALAD BAR HERE. An air-raid siren flared in the background. Rachel had only ever heard this sound in movies and was surprised the sirens were used in real life. As she and Luke jammed a set of old curtains into the last remaining cracks in the shattered door and Karen duct-taped the tablecloths in place around the barricade, making the door as airtight as possible, the siren's wail shrank. Their air supply was safe for the time being.

They moved back into the lounge, Luke pausing to pick up the rifle, which he had set down while helping with the door. The sniper had removed his shirt. He was a small man, with pale skin that was inflamed from the chemicals outside. His voice was raspy. He nodded towards his duffle bag. "I'm not going to try and kill you, but I do get to keep my stuff. That's part of the deal."

They stood watching him. Rachel said, "My name is Rachel. This is Luke and Karen and Rick." The sniper grunted. Rachel said, "You look really great for someone who's been through what you've just been through. You look really relaxed. I wish I had what you have."

"Tell *Rick* to take his gun off me."

"I can't do that," said Rick.

The sniper looked around behind the bar, at the ceiling, and at the rear area. Something by the cash register caught his eye, and he laughed. He went to the machine and ripped a magazine clipping off the side. It was a colour photo of Leslie Freemont looking inspirationally forty-five degrees off camera, up into the sky. "What the hell is a picture of this freak doing here?"

"That's Leslie Freemont," Rick said.

"I know damn well who it is." He reached into his

duffle bag and removed one of the bloodied rags. Rachel took another look and saw that the material was actually a blood-clotted shock of white hair. The sniper threw Leslie Freemont's scalp onto the bar. "I know how to deal with false prophets."

Player One

The thing about the future is that it's full of things happening, whereas the present so often feels stale and dead. We dread the future but it's what we have. I can tell you here that while Luke keeps the shotgun aimed at the sniper's head, Karen and Rick will duct-tape him to a chair. On completion the group will learn that the sniper is a talker. He will say to the assembled group, "Imagine, all of you, feeling more powerful and more capable of falling in love with life every new day instead of being scared and sick and not knowing whether to stay under a sheet or venture forth into the cold of the day."

The sniper will say, "Imagine no longer being trapped in a dying and corrupt world, but instead making a new one from this one's shattered remnants."

The sniper will say, "Imagine that for an unknown reason you have begun to rapidly lose your memory. You now no longer know what month it is, say, or what type of car you drive, or the season, or the food in your refrigerator, or the names of the flowers."

The sniper will suck in some breath and say, "Quickly, quickly your memory freezes — a tiny, perfect iceberg, all memories frozen, *locked*. Your family. Your sex. Your name. All of it turned into a silent ice block. You are free of memory. You now look at the world with the eyes of an embryo, not knowing, only seeing and hearing. Then suddenly the ice melts, your memory begins returning. The ice is in a pond — it thaws and the water warms and water lilies grow from your memories and fish swim within them. And that pond is you."

Finally, the sniper will say, "Everyone wants to go to heaven, but nobody wants to die."

At that point, Karen will blink, while Rick, newly in love with Rachel, is thinking, *You know, shoot me if you want, you whack-job. It doesn't matter because I'll die a happy man. Chemical cloud? Eat me! I don't care, because you can't corrode the love that protects me like a triple-wax polish on my old Barracuda. Booze? Don't even try killing me this time, booze. It's over between you and me. I am a man in love, and for this brief chunk of time, life and death have become the same thing — living is the same as dying as is living as is dying as is —*

This is when the power will go off.

Luke's first instinct when the lights go out will be to shout, "My jewels!" — a joke that always got a laugh when the church's power kept failing after the ice storms a few years back. But a joke is not what's going to be needed when everything turns black — or not even black — it will feel like the world turned itself *off* — this relentless entropy that's swallowing Luke's universe like an angry time-space wormhole. *Everything I can think of*, he will think, *is going, item by item by item*: cars, electricity, Cancun holidays, frozen Lean Cuisine dinners, the give-a-penny/take-a-penny jar at the local Esso station — hell, the whole Esso station — police safety, water out of taps, clean air — it will feel to Luke as if the world now has rapid-onset Alzheimer's and is itself systematically disintegrating. His father would have loved this sensation of End of Days. His father wanted to go to heaven and would have cheerfully taken the next bus there without hesitation. That poor, dumb bastard who scared or insulted away or betrayed all the people who otherwise ought to have been in his life, and who somehow managed to turn Luke into himself.

But *no*, Luke will reject what is happening as being the end of the world, and he will reject what has up until now seemed to be his inevitable conversion into his father . . . his father, who would have said, with a pathetic false English accent — like, who was he trying to impress, anyway? — his family, who knew that Caleb had only once been to England, in 1994 for three nights at a Heathrow Airport hotel for a symposium on the subject "Man in the Age of the Rampant Machine" — machines! In 19forGod'ssake94! Caleb, who would most predictably have said, there, in the Airport Camelot cocktail lounge, "I said to the man who stood at the gate of the New Year, 'Give me a light that I may tread safely into the unknown.' And he replied: 'Go out into the darkness and put your hand into the hand of God. That shall be to you better than light and safer than any known way.'"

Rachel will stare at Leslie Freemont's scalp and she will think it resembles a very large dissected white mouse — or maybe a rat — but Rachel doesn't like rats, because rats might bite her, whereas mice would never hurt her. Rachel won't, however, be freaked out by the scalp. The scalp's presence will make her enter her clinical mode, as though she were in the local medical supplier's lab wearing one of those freshly laundered coats they hand out that smell faintly like lavender, their crisp, starchy fabric on her forearms giving her the happy sensation of an itch being properly scratched. But the scalp? It's just a specimen, and, as it can't hurt her or enter the one-metre invisible circular comfort zone around her body — the zone within which it might touch her, breathe on her, or offer any sort of swift temperature change — Rachel will remain in a heightened but calm state. She knows the others are frightened, but she knows better than to tell them to not be afraid — doing so has gotten her in trouble in the past. And what on earth could there possibly be to fear from falling down into Daffy Duck's cartoon hole?

Hello, My Name Is: Monster

Karen

Karen stares at the black-haired sniper, with his blistered face and seemingly powder-burned forearms. Her body still shaking, Karen asks her duct-taped prisoner, "Okay, then, what's your name?"

"You tell me. What do you think my name ought to be? What do I look like? Am I a Jason? A Justin? A *Craig*?"

Karen begins wondering, in earnestness, if he looks more like a Justin than a Jason or a Craig — and then chides herself for so quickly going in a mundane direction. *This guy truly believes he did good by killing Leslie Freemont.* Karen wonders when and where Leslie was scalped, and if his assistant, Tara, escaped.

Luke blurts out, "Monsters don't need names."

"Then that's my new name. *Hello, my name is: Monster.*"

"Very funny."

"Very well, then, my name is Bertis."

"We should just shoot you, Bertis," says Rick.

Bertis is cavalier. "Then shoot me. I'm at the end of one aspect of my life, but also at the beginning of some unknown secret that will reveal itself to me soon."

Karen thinks, *What if God exists, but he just doesn't like people very much?*

Rick asks, "Why were you stalking Leslie Freemont?"

"He was a fraud. He had it coming."

"Why did you shoot the others, then?"

"Because I can see clearly enough to decide who lives and who dies." He pauses and surveys the room. "Oh, don't give me those faces. They died because it was their time. Their leaders are dead. History has abandoned them. The past is a joke. Me and what I'm doing is what was meant to happen next."

"Who died and made you God?"

Bertis laughed. "Don't be a child. Grow up. The people I shot bothered God. They angered Him. They wasted His time. Look at modern culture. Look at Americans — they're like children, always asking for miracle this or love that, or *Gee, I tried my hardest*. But God created an ordered world. By constantly bombarding Him for miracles, we're asking Him to unravel the fabric of the world. A world of continuous miracles would be a cartoon. In repayment for being an endless nuisance, Americans have become a quarter-billion oil-soaked mallard ducks. I didn't know this oil crisis was going to happen when I woke up this morning and vowed to take out that quack, Freemont — it's one of life's little bonuses."

Karen says, "You can't lump a quarter-billion people all in together. That's absurd. Those quarter-billion people have almost nothing in common except that they've been told they have lots in common."

Bertis looks at Karen. "I like you. But you're wrong. People are pretty much all the same — unless they've achieved Salvation, at which point they all become one person, one source of light. We humans have infinitely more in common with each other than we do differ-ence. Look at this bar. Look at this hotel, the airport. Ever wonder why they sell flags and family coats of arms and KISS ME, I'M ITALIAN T-shirts in airports and tourist traps? Ever wonder why religious groups hang out there? Because a plane trip takes you away from all the things that make you comfortable. A plane trip exposes you to situations and landscapes unthinkable until recent history, moments of magnificence and banality that dissolve what few itty-bitty molecules of individuality you possess. After a plane trip, you need to rebuild your ego, to shore up your sense of being unique. That's why religions target airports to find new recruits. You —" He nods at Rick. "You're a bartender. You do nothing but watch people dissolve in front of you all day. Or scramble themselves with booze. And I bet you have no illusions about what goes on in the hotel next door."

"You're right on that."

Karen remembers her assignation with Warren, which now feels as if it happened three weeks ago.

Bertis purses his lips and X-rays the door area to see the hotel behind it. "Nasty, *nasty* hotel. Cracked-out teenagers watching trash TV and eating sugar. Fornicating on towels decorated with Disney cartoons and brands of beer. And maybe on a good day you'll find a prophet alone in an empty room on the top floor, the elevator rusted shut; a prophet stripped of his founding visions, forced to live in a world robbed of values, ideals, and direction."

The four of them stand staring at Bertis, who sits with perfect posture.

"Look at you all. You're a depressing grab bag of pop culture influences and cancelled emotions, driven by the sputtering engine of the most banal form of capitalism. No seasons in your lives — merely industrial production cycles that rule you far better than any tyrant. You keep waiting for the moral of your life to become obvious, but it never does. Work, work, work: No moral. No plot. No *eureka!* Just production schedules and *days.* You might as well all be living inside a photocopier. Your lives are all they're ever going to be."

"I agree with him," says Rachel, sending a ripple through the group.

"Really?" asks Rick, genuinely surprised.

"Not the meaningless bit. But the bits about everyone being the same. I can't tell faces apart. It's hard to tell people apart. I can't distinguish personalities. When my high school yearbook came out, it was like looking at a thousand identical faces. I couldn't even find myself."

"I think you're unique," says Rick.

"You do?"

"I do. It's not just that you're beautiful. It's your mice. And the way you think so hard about everything. I've never seen anyone think so hard in my life."

Rachel confesses, "Earlier, when I was supposed to be looking up the price of oil, I was actually looking up the price of white mice."

"So you feel guilty. We now have official evidence that you're human. Welcome to the club."

"Really? There's a club?"

"No, there isn't. But I'm starting one now, and I welcome you to join me."

Rachel walks over to Rick and says, "Thank you," seemingly hypnotized.

Rick says, "What's the great thing about normal, anyway? What's normal ever done for you?" Rachel smiles.

"So what is it we're supposed to be doing here, then?" Bertis snaps.

"Doing?" she says.

"Are we waiting for the police to show up? Is this some hokey citizen's arrest? Am I going to be brought to justice? I've been outside, and trust me, there won't be any cops here for a week."

Karen asks, "What's it like out there?"

Luke, who's been pretty quiet up to now, says, "Excuse me, Karen." In a flash, he raises the rifle and fires it at the floor in front of Bertis, hitting his foot. Bertis screams, then cries out, "What the hell did you do that for?"

"I had to do *something* to you. I'm sick of waiting for the law. And knowing the courts in this country, instead of sending you to rot in prison, they'll send you to Disney World with a life counsellor and a dozen juice boxes." Luke sets Bertis's rifle down on the bar. He says to Bertis, "That was richly satisfying and you richly deserved it."

"You'll burn for that."

"That from *you* of all people."

The carpet near Bertis's foot resembles a run-over squirrel, but Karen's seen worse. Even though it's hard to be compassionate for Bertis, she goes to the bar and pulls a bottle of vodka down from the mirrored racks. She walks over to Bertis. "I'll sterilize it."

Bertis is inspecting his shattered toe, grimacing. He glowers at the room, and his voice deepens as Karen unscrews the vodka bottle's cap. "You're all of you praying a prayer — a prayer so deep and strong and insistent you hardly know you are praying it. It comes from that better place inside you — the place that remains pure. You never manage to access it, but you know it exists." Bertis glowered at a six-foot-tall cardboard cut-out promoting Chilean wine. "I don't need to justify my actions to the courts of this world. The only valid viewpoint to make any decision from is Eternity."

"Lovely," says Luke.

Bertis squints. "You don't believe in believing, do you?"

"You picked a very strange day to ask me that question."

Rachel says, "Luke was a pastor up until yesterday. Then he lost his faith and stole twenty thousand dollars from his church's bank account and flew here, to this airport, essentially at random." She looks to Luke for confirmation.

"Timing is everything," says Luke. Karen grabs a white linen napkin and tears it down the middle, improvising a bandage, which quickly reddens as she lashes it onto Bertis's toe.

———

Suddenly incapable of processing any more of what was happening to her at the present time, Karen let her mind drift back to that morning, a morning that had begun so full of hope. She remembered packing her toiletries for the flight, looking in the mirror, and thinking, *Karen Dawson, you are a well-nourished, rich-looking white woman. You could burn polka dots onto the mayor's front door with a crème brûlée torch and nobody would bother you. And this Warren fellow will be putty in your hands.* Then she caught herself from a certain angle and saw her mother's face contained within her own — a face now blankened by Alzheimer's, a face resting in an expensive ozone-smelling room in Winnipeg. *Am I going to get Alzheimer's? My genetic counsellor says three chances in four.* Karen's mother was no longer knowable; her mother was gone. Staring at herself in the mirror, Karen wondered, *When do people stop being individuals and turn into generic humans? And from there, when do they stop being human and become vegetable, then mineral?*

Perhaps people are all, in the end, unknowable. But at least some people are loveable, and at least some of them love you. Of course, they can also *stop* loving you. When Kevin fell out of love with her — and into love with another receptionist, no less — Karen wondered, *How many married men are out there whispering like truffle pigs in the ears of temps by the office snack-vending machine? She wondered, How many are spending their noon hours in a motel down by the lake? And their wives — how many are starting to drink Baileys while folding laundry? How many are almost sick with jealousy over "that bright young gal" who's turned the marketing department upside down with fresh ideas? That bright young gal with a future as big as Montana and legs like Bambi's mother's.*

As she looked in the mirror, Karen thought, *Okay, so there's no permanent love in this world, and you can never really know anyone, but at least there's heaven. Perhaps heaven is being in love and the feeling never stops — the feeling of intimacy never stops — you feel intimate forever.*

Zipping up her sandwich bag filled with cosmetics in airline-approved bottles smaller than 1.5 ounces, Karen began wondering if she was past love — if she had felt pretty much all the emotions she was ever likely to feel, and from that point on it was reruns. She wondered, *Which is lonelier: to be single and lonely or to be lonely within a dead relationship? Is it totally pathetic to be single and lonely and to be jealous of someone who is lonely inside a dead relationship? I feel like the punchline to a joke I might have told ten years ago.*

What had happened to her earlier good spirits? She ought to have been whistling ditties to the love gods, but now she felt manless and marooned as she contemplated a life of repetitive labour, a few thousand more microwaved dinners followed by a coffin. What a wretched tailspin to have fallen into. She chalked it up to nerves over meeting Warren.

At the breakfast table, Karen learned that Casey had chosen that morning to unveil an even more extreme version of her blue and black hair: a set of blue extensions that bulked it up, doubling its volume. But Karen was not going to be roped into a style squabble. Not today. Not over a bowl of oatmeal.

"What do you think of my new do?" Casey asked.

"It's great. It's fine," Karen said.

"It's part of my campaign to become immortal."

"How's that, Casey? Pass me the brown sugar."

"History only remembers people who invent new hairdos: Julius Caesar. Einstein. Hitler. Marilyn Monroe. Why bother with conquering Europe or discovering nuclear science when all you need is a bit of style innovation? If Marie Curie had given a bit more attention to her appearance she'd have been on the ten-dollar bill."

"Very clever."

Casey senses that Karen's not in a fighting mood. "Mom, what do you think happens to you after you die?"

"What do you mean?"

"Do you believe in something specific, like a religion,

or do you think maybe there's a warm cosmic flow, followed by the total extinction of your being?"

"Casey, this isn't something I expected to be discussing on a Tuesday morning."

"On *Star Trek: Generations*, Soran said, 'Time is the fire in which we burn.' Imagine that, Mom, burning inside a fire of time."

"It's Tuesday fricking morning, Casey. And you know I've got a big day ahead of me. You tell me, what do you think about an afterlife?"

"I don't know," said Casey. "If I was truly practical and green and into recycling and all of that, I'd request that you put my body into a big pot and then reduce it until it turns into that soup powder they put in your ramen noodles."

"But you're not practical."

"No, I am not. I want to be buried, not cremated. And no coffin. I repeat, no coffin — just put me in the dirt."

"Just dirt? That's kind of ick."

"Not true. Being soil is a good idea — I'd be moist and granular, like raspberry oatmeal muffins." Casey scraped up the remains of her oatmeal. "Kendra from my twirling class says death is like a spa resort where everything is pre-decided for you and all you have to do is lie back and submit to the regime."

"Kendra sounds a bit lazy to me."

"Kendra is wicked lazy."

"Let's go. I can drop you off on the way to the airport."

"But you haven't told me what you think about death!"

"Well, Casey, I don't remember where I was before I was born, so why should I be worried about where I'll go after I die? When we die, we have no choice but to join every living thing that's ever existed — and ever will."

"You're getting cosmic, Mom. Get cosmic more often. But what do you really think of my hair?"

"In the car. Now. You're not going to goad me into trashing your hair."

Since then, Karen had crossed a continent, had a failed romantic liaison, witnessed a murder, participated in the collapse of the Western world, and taken a religious nutcase as a prisoner.

Rousing herself from her reverie, Karen looked at her dead phone. She noticed that Rick and Rachel had left the room, and that Luke was now guarding Bertis with the shotgun. She thought of Casey, at home watching smoke plumes spout from around the city, lashing together heaven and earth. She sat across the table from him and said, "You know, Mr. Bertis, if you have something to say, I'm listening."

Rick

Rick is in love. How quickly the universe disposed of Leslie Freemont to make room in his heart for the beautiful young Rachel. Nothing about the current situation fazes him. He feels no fear, just warmth. He feels as if he can shoot laser beams from the tips of his fingers and, correctly aiming at the right person, make them feel holy. He feels like a superhero called Holy Man.

And he has a shotgun. That helps, too. And Luke shooting off Bertis's left toe — that was intense, but Bertis deserved far worse.

Rick detects shades of Leslie Freemont in Bertis's speech patterns. In fact, Bertis is a better Leslie Freemont than Leslie Freemont ever was. He is about to raise the subject when Rachel twists her head and sniffs like a border collie. "There's a chemical leak. The outside is getting in. It's coming from out back."

Sensing an opportunity, Rick takes it. He passes the shotgun to Luke, saying, "We're going to fix the leak. Come on, Rachel."

Rachel asks, "You shut off all the overhead vents, correct?"

"Tight as a drum."

"It's coming from over there . . ."

Rick follows Rachel to the rear storage area, where that morning he'd been getting a weekend's worth of empties boxed for the recycler. Above the crates is a small louvred window, slats open. "That's the leak," Rachel says. "Can you reach it?"

"I'll have to stand on the crates."

"I'll stand below and make sure they're stable. And I'll hold you." The chemical dust coming in feels like ground glass in Rick's eyes and throat. Rachel throws Rick a bar rag to cover his face. He climbs up on the crates and stands on his tiptoes, Rachel steadying him at his knees as he shuts the window. "There. It's closed," Rick says.

But Rachel doesn't let go of his knees. And Rick doesn't want her to let go. He wants the moment to last forever. This would be his heaven: the moment when the spark ignites and you know it's all going to happen, that your instincts were correct.

The rear area is quiet. Rick can hear both Rachel's and his own breathing. He's fully aroused and knows it will soon be time to come on strong.

Rachel says, "Nobody's ever kissed me before."

"Oh?" Rick says, staring at the closed window.

"No. Often, if people even touch me, I scream. I know I shouldn't, but I can't stop myself."

Rick hops off the crates and stands directly in front of Rachel, face to face. Rachel inspects his face. She says, "I see you have a scar beside your eye."

"I got stabbed."

"Stabbed in the face?"

"It was a stupid fight. It was a long time ago. I don't do that anymore. Fight, I mean. Only when I go on a bender, but I haven't been on one for fourteen months now."

"Did it hurt?"

"What — getting stabbed? Not really. You'd think it would, but no. In fact, it was kind of cool. Like my soul jumped out of my skin for a second, like a salmon jumping out of a river."

Rachel says, "I'm glad you have an identifying trait I can recognize you by."

"Yeah?" Rick can feel Rachel's breath on his face, like the air before a late-afternoon summer storm.

"You look very relaxed," Rachel says.

"Yeah?"

"Maybe. I can't tell, really. They told us in normalcy training that if you tell normal people they look relaxed, they actually do relax. It's a coping tactic."

Rick kisses Rachel. She doesn't respond at first, and he wonders if he's wrecked everything and come across as a perv, but then she ignites and practically bites his face off with passion. Rachel's so energetic it's actually freaking Rick out a bit, but she's young and her reptile cortex knows what it wants. And Rick is older and knows how to deliver. And he's loving it, getting down and dirty in the back of the bar as if he were young again. It's just the two of them in their own little universe, and suddenly everything in the world makes sense, because without the crap and the death and the drudgery and the endlessness of life, it would be impossible for passion to exist.

Nothing very, very good and nothing very, very bad
lasts for very, very long. A half-hour later, Rachel and
Rick were on the floor. Their clothes were relatively
clean, and Rick was oddly proud that he had been such
a good custodian of the space. And who'd have thought
the storeroom, with light filtering in from the main bar
area, could look and feel romantic? Rachel turned her
head and looked at Rick. "Rick, why was Leslie Freemont so important to you?"

"Leslie Freemont? Honestly?"

"Yes."

Rick looked up at the ceiling. "Well . . . because starting a few years back, I began feeling like my life was no
longer my own. I felt like I was this person stuck inside
the body of someone named Rick. I had access to his
memories and knowledge, but I wasn't Rick."

"Do you mean schizophrenia? Or dissociative identity disorder?"

"No. Those would be interesting. Those would be
fixable with medicine. What I have can't be fixed by
medicine — or booze — even though I tried. I mean,
I had a kid and a wife, and then, once my marriage
ended, I looked around me and everyone in my life had
changed — grown older, become different, moved on.
So I tried to avoid life by sleeping all the time, but my
problems invaded my dream life. Man, that sucked. And
then there was the drinking. And I became invisible to
people under thirty. And I learned that women want

guys the same age as me, but without my mileage. I
had to learn to cope with the knowledge that my chance
to make big strokes in life was over. I was never going to
be rich or really good at doing something — anything.
So I scraped together what I could and got a truck and
tools and started a landscaping business. I was kind of
making a go of it, and then it all got stolen — the truck
and the tools — and I stopped wanting to exist anymore."

"Suicidal impulses?"

"No. I just didn't want to exist. Sometimes it feels as
if everything in life is just something we haul into the
grave. And then I saw this Freemont guy on TV and
it was like he could see the hole in my soul and had a
way to fix it. He was so confident. People liked him. He
knew how to succeed. He could prove to me that life is
bigger than we give it credit for — that something huge
can just happen out of the blue. We can enter a world
where all the women wear those nice, clean sweaters
from Banana Republic and sing along to the radio in key,
a world where the guys drive Chevy Camaros and never
stumble or screw up or look stupid. I thought Leslie
Freemont's ideas would make me feel young again."

"I don't think your face reads as old."

"That's an interesting way of phrasing it. But I am.
Old. Trust me."

"There's that expression normal people use: You're
only as young as you feel."

"I beg to differ, Rachel. When you're young, you feel
like life hasn't yet begun, like life is scheduled to begin

next week, next month, next year, after the holidays —
whenever. But suddenly you're old, and the scheduled
life never arrived. I find myself asking, 'Well, then,
exactly what was it I was doing with all that time I had
before I thought my life would begin?'"

Rachel said, "I think we should go back to the bar,
Rick."

"No way. I want to stay here forever. Right here. Right
now. With you."

"There's a sniper out there, and Karen and Luke might
want help guarding him."

"I know."

Rachel got onto her knees and looked at Rick. Rick
kissed his fingertip and touched it to her lips. He said,
"You know, I have always liked the idea of Superman,
because I like the idea that there is one person in the
world who doesn't do bad things. And who is able to fly."

"Superman is absurd," said Rachel. "The notion that
people can fly is ridiculous. In order to fly, we would
have to have chest muscles that stretched out in front of
us for five or six feet."

Rick smiled. "I used to pray to God. I asked, 'Please,
God, just make me a bird, a graceful white bird free of
shame and taint and fear of loneliness, and give me
other white birds among which to fly, and give me a sky
so big and wide that if I never wanted to land, I would
never have to.'" Rick looked into Rachel's eyes.

Rachel said, "But you can't be a bird. You're a person.
People can't be birds."

Rick smiled again. "But instead God gave me you, Rachel, and you are here with me to listen to these words as I speak them."

Rachel blinked and looked Rick in the face. Rick was unsure whether he'd connected. Rachel said, "Rick, in normalcy class we learned that people are often most attractive and charismatic when they are confused and when they think that nobody could possibly like them."

"Are they?"

"Yeah. Please, Rick. Stand up and come with me. Okay?"

"Roger." Rick stood up. "What I like about you, Rachel, is that I never know what's going to come out of your mouth next."

Rachel said, "Rick, when Donald Duck traded his wings for arms, do you think he thought he was trading up or trading down?"

"Donald Duck? Trading down, obviously. Who wouldn't want to fly?"

Luke

Bertis says, "Everyone wants to go to heaven, but nobody wants to die."

Karen blinks.

The power goes out, and nobody is surprised. A dribble of light comes in through the barricaded doors, but nothing useful, only enough to allow Karen to locate a box of table candles and matches from behind the bar; light is somewhat restored.

Bertis looks across the room at Luke and changes his tone. "So, you're a thief?"

"Looks like it."

"Your twenty grand's probably not worth much by now. How ironic. Your flock will be angry."

Luke is nonchalant. "They've got bigger things to worry about. They probably don't even know yet that I did it. And when they learn that the money's not worth anything anymore, I'll be off the hook. Didn't plan it that way, but that's how it rolled."

Karen gets up and goes to Bertis, dribbling more vodka over the remains of his toe. Bertis's face betrays a sting as he says, "You should have stolen something more purely valuable, Luke. Maybe some DNA cloned from the Pope's Band-Aid — or a dab of antimatter from that supercollider thingy over in Switzerland."

Luke says, "Okay, you've scored your point. Want me to shoot off your other toe?" The candlelit room and the shotgun make the room feel like a painting from a few centuries back — a domestic interior. Some dead hares and partridges would look at home in the environment.

Bertis is snide: "Oops. Looks like power's gone to your head."

Karen intervenes. "Fellas, look, stop it right now."

Luke knows that Karen is right to stop this from escalating. But *wow!* . . . It's late afternoon and Luke is now a prison guard in a cocktail lounge filled with what smells like burning snow tires leaking in from the outside. How did his life come to this? Twenty-four hours earlier he was . . . *What was I doing? I know: trying to decide if a McDonald's Filet-o-Fish was eco-friendly and whether to upgrade my cable package and put it on the church's tab. Church: how strange to think of it right now.* Luke is in the foxhole, but it's not making him question his newly found atheism. He asks Bertis, "Why would you kill Leslie Freemont?"

"Why? Because he wanted to go to heaven without dying."

"Excuse me — explain that to me."

"He was a prisoner of the world. He thought earthly happiness was all we needed. 'Power Dynamics Seminar System.' What the hell is *that*? Leslie Freemont thought humans saw themselves as bottomless wells of creativity and uniqueness. But God refuses to see any one person as unique in his or her relationship to Him. Nobody's special. And life on earth is just a bus stop on the way to greater glory or greater suffering."

Bertis is pushing many of Luke's father buttons.

When Luke was growing up, Caleb had spoken with

the same evangelical fervour as Bertis. That old bastard, Caleb, dead three years now, reclaimed by the soil, by the planet, by the solar system. Why would someone have a son just so he could have a sparring partner? So that he could create a smaller-scale version of himself? At one point Luke thought he'd gotten over Caleb's spiritual belittlement — in his teens, when he likened God and Caleb to the weather: You may not like the weather, but it has nothing to do with you. You just happen to be there. Deal with it. Sadness and grief are part of being human and always will be. That's not for one person to fix. Luke became the bad boy every mother fears her daughter will get entangled with: unlikely bouts in which he hot-wired cars behind the tire shop, and times when he'd vanish for days doing ecstasy with the unpopular kids who smoked beside the lacrosse field dugout. Luke told himself that belief in God was just a way to deal with things that were out of your control. His father said that was pathetic, that it did nothing to address the moral obligations of the individual.

Luke realizes that his rebellious phase was a necessary step on his path to becoming a pastor. Nobody wants advice from a goody two-shoes.

Karen asks Bertis, "Are you married?"

Bertis snaps, "No. You?"

Karen says, "No. But I was. Were you ever?"

Bertis pauses long enough to make it clear that the answer is yes.

Luke says, "She abandoned you, didn't she?"

Bertis flips out. "How dare *you* talk to me about my life like that?"

Ahhh . . . Luke has seen this before: hyperfaith abandonment syndrome — people, usually guys, going too gung-ho on faith after someone leaves them. Just another OCD, not much different from hoarding newspapers or compulsive handwashing.

Bertis says, "I don't see a ring on *your* finger, Pastor Luke," and Luke is taken aback. "Ah. So now I've pushed one of *your* buttons. You don't strike me as queer, so I'm going to have to guess that you're damaged goods somehow. And you know I'm right, don't you? Karen, what do you think — is Luke damaged goods?"

Luke thinks, *Man, this guy is good at creating awkward moments*. Then he looks at Karen. She's standing halfway between him and Bertis, with her arms crossed. And he can tell from her face that she really does want to know why he has ended up alone.

"Let me get this straight. With everything that has happened — and is happening — you both want to know why I'm still single?"

Karen and Bertis nod.

"Okay, then . . ."

Why are *you single, Luke?*

———

Luke thought about this. *Why?*

"Well, my dad was a pastor and so I rebelled — yes,

son of a preacher man and all that, and let me tell you, it really is catnip to women — but then by twenty I'd seen enough of the world to know that we need to protect ourselves from ourselves, and I came back to the church. And . . ." Luke became as wistful as it's possible to be while pointing a shotgun at someone's aorta. "I knew I was a soul in trouble — that's how I viewed it at the time. But when I went back to the church, the women there wanted a goody-goody, a private express lane to God, Ten Commandments or less. And the thing is, I was no longer a bad boy, but despite becoming a pastor I was never a goody-goody either. And nobody in the *middle* ever liked me. And you know, I've been here on earth for thirty-something years, and I don't think there is even one person who ever really *knew* me, which is a private disgrace. I don't even know if people are knowable."

With those last words, Karen became totally focused on him.

"Figuring this stuff out takes time. I'm rambling. I'm human; I'm still trapped inside of . . . *time* . . . trapped inside the world of *things*."

"Don't stop," said Karen. "You're not rambling. Keep talking."

"Okay, so, yes — I probably am damaged goods and, yes, I think I am a broken person. I seriously question the road I've taken, and I endlessly rehash the compromises I've made in my life." Luke sat down at the table across from Bertis. Karen sat between them.

"Go on," said Bertis.

"At one point, I really felt like I had a soul — it felt like a small glowing ember buried deep inside my guts. It felt real."

"So then, who dumped you?" Bertis asked, adding, "Takes one to know one."

"Does it matter?"

"It does."

"No, it doesn't, because none of it matters, because no matter what I do I'm going to inherit Alzheimer's from my bastard father." Karen's eyes flared open wider. "That's the real reason for most things in my life that go sideways. The day I turn fifty-five, my universe is going to start erasing itself. So what's the point of doing anything?"

They heard some noises from out back.

Karen asked, "What is that?"

Bertis said, "I think those two are getting it on."

More noise.

Karen asked, "She *is* over eighteen, right?"

Bertis looked at Luke, whose face featured a small pout. "You're jealous, aren't you?" asked Bertis. "Let me guess — you thought she liked *you* better."

Karen butted in. "More important to me right now, Bertis, is what is your deal?"

"Excuse me?"

"You. Rifle. Killing people."

"Karen, I can see you're not a believer."

"In what?"

"God. A great truth."

"I'm listening."

"You need to accept that your current path is death in disguise."

"Go on."

"You need to look at the universe as a place filled with huge rocks and massive globs of burning gas that obey laws, but then ask yourself, to what end? Remind yourself that we are living creatures — we have mystical impulses, impulses that tell us the universe is a place charged with mystery, not just a vacuum filled with rocks and lava. We're all born separated from God — over and over, life makes sure to inform us of that — and yet we're all real: We have names, we have lives. We mean something. We must."

"Okay."

"Your life is too easy, Karen. You've been tricked into not questioning your soul. Do you know this?"

"I'm listening."

"Karen, tell me, what is the *you* of you? Where do you begin and end? This *you* thing — is it an invisible silk woven from your memories? Is it a spirit? Is it electric? What exactly is it? Does it know that there exists a light within us all — a light brighter than the sun, a light inside the mind? Does the real Karen know that, when we sleep at night, when we walk across a field and see a tree full of sleeping birds, when we tell small lies to our friends, when we make love, we are performing acts of surgery on our souls? All this damage and healing and shock that happens inside of us, the result of which is unfathomable. But imagine if you could see the light, the *souls* inside everybody you see — at Loblaws, on the dog-walking path, at the library — all those souls, bright lights, blinding you, perhaps. But they are *there*."

Luke rolled his eyes. "You talk kind of pretty for a monster."

Bertis swivelled his head to Luke. "You keep quiet." He turned back to Karen. "Karen, I like you, and this could be the day you finally wake up from the long, dead sleep that has been your life until now."

"So, you're telling me I've been asleep for some four decades? What was it I was doing all that time, then?"

"I don't know. Being a part of the world — being in time rather than in Eternity. I can hear your soul, Karen. I can hear it just a bit, creaking like a house shifting ever so slightly off its foundations. In my heart it feels like that moment once a year when I smell the air and know fall is here — except it's not the fall, Karen, it's forever. Take down the barricade and look out the door there. Look out into this terrifying and gleaming new century, where the sun burns the eyes of innocents, where the sun burns whenever and wherever it wants, where night no longer provides respite. Where are you to find mercy in a place like that? Where will you find the correct path? There will be anarchy. Office buildings will collapse, and when they dig through the rubble, the people who were inside will be found compressed into diamonds from the force. The diamond is your soul."

Luke heard footsteps, and Rick and Rachel entered the bar.

"Ah," said Bertis. "The lovebirds."

Rick came in talking. "Hey, you — Bertis — how did you get up on the roof of this place, anyway?"

"There's an Ontario Hydro truck with a cherry picker beside the east wall."

"Well, *that* was simple."

Rachel

Rachel asks Karen, "Karen, is this what dreams are like?"

"Huh? What are you talking about?"

"Right now, like this — there are no lights, and yet things are still happening. Is this what dreams are like?"

"You mean you've never had a dream?"

"Not that I remember. Dreams are for normal people. I just sleep."

"That's so sad."

"Why would it be sad?"

"Because . . ." Karen paused. ". . . Because dreams are part of being alive."

"I think dreams are a biological response to the fact that our planet rotates, and that for a billion years earth has had both a night and a day."

"You're being unfair to dreams. They can't be neatly put in a box like that. They can be wonderful."

"But if you accept dreams, you also have to accept nightmares, and I know nightmares are bad things. And if dreams are so special, why is it that no person or company has ever tried to make a drug that leads to better dreaming? Sleeping pills, yes, but dreaming pills? Have scientists even asked that question?"

More candles are lit and Rachel sees Rick's face glowing orange above a bowl lamp covered in white mesh and lit by a candle inside. He's showing teeth, but the corners of his mouth are upturned, so she knows he is smiling at her. "No, Rachel, it's not a dream," he says, "just real life. Here. You. Me. Us. Now. And dig these cheesy candles, like we're eating spaghetti at the restaurant with Lady and the Tramp." Rachel is pretty sure she can now distinguish Rick from Luke. At this moment, it's Rick's voice that determines his identity. Rick — the father of her child as of mere moments ago.

As she helps Rick light candles around the room, Rachel wonders if he fathered her child because she is beautiful or because he is in love with her or because he is, as her mother would say, a dog. But how can a man be a dog? Or vice versa? And even if they could, why would being a dog be bad? Rachel's father says that if cats were double their usual size, they'd probably be illegal and you'd have to shoot them, but even if dogs were three times as big, they'd still be good friends to people. Rachel sees that as a good way of comparing the two species.

Rachel replays her memories of the previous half-hour — both her normal memories and the backup copies generated by her brain's amygdala. When Rick asked Rachel to come help him fix the leak that was allowing toxins into the building, she was happy to help. And then something new entered her life, something she couldn't explain. Rick was standing on some plastic crates and Rachel was holding his legs, keeping him stable as he shut the window's louvres. But when he was finished, he didn't get down — and Rachel didn't let go of his legs, even though Rick no longer required stability. She somehow knew that if she let go of him she would

miss out on something she might never again experience. She felt, well . . . the thing is, she *felt*. She had
feelings she had no words for — which is how normal
people must go through life, ad-libbing through unclear
situations, trying to label things that can't be labelled.

Rachel thought, *Okay, God, I've been hearing a lot
about you today. So this is the one time I'm ever going to
speak to you, so you'd better be listening. Dear God, please
send me a sign that this is how it feels to be human. Dear
God, please send me a sign that this is how it feels to be
a* woman. *Dear God, oh please, for once in my life let me
be like the others — just this once and I'll never bug you
again. I might even believe in you. But if you're going to do
this, you have to do it now. It can't be later. It has to be now,
while I'm standing here in the storage room of a cocktail bar
near an airport in the early half of the twenty-first century
in the middle of the North American continent. It has to be
now, while I'm holding these legs in my arms, feeling the
muscles move within them, feeling their heat. I'm touching
another person, and I don't want to run away or scream —
in fact, I want the opposite. So there you go, God — it's all
I've ever wanted and all I'll ever ask you for.*

And God gave Rachel what she wanted.

———

Rachel looked out over the candlelit lounge. No one
was talking, so Rachel said, "Sometimes when things
are quiet at home, I'll play Scrabble with my family, but

we remove some of the vowels to make the game more challenging. Do you have a Scrabble game here, Rick?"

"Nope. But can I get you a fresh ginger ale?"

"Thank you, Rick."

The lounge was getting humid, and Rachel disliked that — the humidity felt like strangers were touching her. A part of her wanted to retreat into her Happy Place, but after recent events, the place no longer had the appeal it once did. Rachel figured she now had to be pregnant — she had to be, because she'd followed all the rules for getting pregnant. And besides, people can't take babies to Happy Places because babies need to be cared for all the time. And strangely, going to the Happy Place would mean going back in time in a way that wasn't good. Rachel had come too far in the past few hours — she had earned her right to be a part of the world. And besides, God had given her what she wanted. Perhaps God was the Happy Place and she'd been mis-labelling Him all her life.

The blister-faced Bertis looked at her and said, "So, Rachel, what do *you* believe in?"

"Me? I believe in God."

Bertis seemed surprised. Everyone did. "You do?"

Rick looked at her. "Really?"

"Oh yes."

Rick said, "But I thought God was . . . I mean . . . you're not really the God type."

"No. You're thinking of the autism spectrum personality cliché. I think God is real."

Luke asked if she'd always believed in God.

"No. It's a new belief."

"Oh. But an hour ago you were asking us why normal people . . ."

Rachel saw where Luke was going. "People change, Luke."

"Okay, but then, do you also believe in evolution?"

"Of course."

"Doesn't one belief cancel out the other?" Karen asked.

Rachel replied, "Not at all. God made the world, and how He went about doing it is whatever it took to get the job done. So it involved fossils and dinosaurs and billions of years. If that's what was required to create our world, then what is the big problem? The world is here. We live in it."

Luke asked, "You have no trouble with the time frames involved — all that time?"

"Luke, human beings were probably not meant to think about time. It's that simple. When people think about time too much, it always seems to cause bad feelings. Infinity is the worst concept of all. What was God thinking when He invented infinity?"

Rachel was secretly loving God. She loved the way God could be used to answer all questions. She no longer had to think things through — although this was probably not the spirit in which one was supposed to embrace belief. She wondered what the fellow members of the Fifty Thousand Mouse Club would make of her conversion — if it would make them see her as less scientifically credible.

Bertis looked at Rick and said, "Hey there, Fornicator. First you made her a fallen woman, but then you redeemed yourself by making her a believer. Good work."

"I had nothing to do with this God thing. I have no idea where it came from."

"Mysterious ways and all that," said Bertis. "So, Rachel, you and I are friends now."

"We are?"

"Yes, we are. We share the most important thing in common: our belief."

"I guess we do."

Rick said, "Don't even try to lure her down your road, dickwad."

"My road? Rick, may I remind you that you have no road at all? If I were to accompany you, to follow you, where might we be going?" He looked at Rachel. "We, at least, have a path, don't we?"

"A path?"

Karen said, "Rachel can't understand metaphors."

"Oh. So I can't tell her that she now has a new set of eyes, capable of seeing miraculous new visions?"

"You could, but she wouldn't get it. Besides, I read medical journals during my lunch break, and whenever surgeons give vision to adults born blind, it always goes horribly wrong."

"Really?"

"Really. The newly sighted never get the hang of it — the way objects move in space and time, colours. Even something as simple as lettuce can scare the pants off them."

"I still like you, even though you're depressing," said Bertis.

"Why do you keep telling me you like me?"

Luke said, "It's an old trick called flattery. He thinks you're a potential convert, so he's buttering you up."

"Buttering?" Rachel asked.

"It's a metaphor," said Luke and Karen in stereo.

Suddenly there was a thump from the direction of the front door, and everybody jumped, startled.

Rick said, "Stand back." He put his back against the wall, shotgun in his right hand, and scootched doorward.

When the noise came again, this time Rachel placed it as someone ramming themselves against the cigarette machine inside the shattered glass door.

Karen said, "It may be the police."

Rick said, "*Shh,*" and scootched closer still.

Bertis turned to Rachel and whispered, "Rachel, could you cut me loose here?"

"No."

"I'm in great pain, Rachel, and sitting up is making it unbearable. I need to lie down on my back and reduce the blood pressure to my lower body. One believer *has* to help another."

"I'll undo your legs and put the chair back on the floor. You'll be lying down, sort of."

"Good. Do it quietly."

Karen hissed at Rick, "Can you see anything?"

Rick shook his head.

Luke looked at Rachel, who was cutting the duct tape from Bertis's legs. "What the . . . Rachel, *stop!*"

"Luke, I'm only undoing his legs so his blood can circulate properly."

Bertis said, "It's just my legs. I need to lie down. It's to help my toe. The one you shot off."

Luke glared at Bertis. "Okay, Rachel, lean him on his back, or whatever it is he wants. But don't untape his hands."

As she tilted Bertis's chair backwards to the ground, Rachel looked at his hands, which were peeling slightly from the chemicals — no wedding ring, a Medic-Alert bracelet, calluses on his fingertips.

Rick cautiously pulled back a tablecloth to look out the door, then shouted, "Holy Christ — it's a kid! A teenager. Quick! Help me get this crap away from the door."

Luke indicated that he would keep standing guard over Bertis, and Rachel and Karen ran to help Rick pull the cigarette machine, the furniture, and the other clutter away from the door. Rachel saw a teenage boy covered in pink dust. His eyes and mouth had been rubbed clean, but they were flaring red.

Rick reached through the door frame and pulled the boy inside.

"Good God," said Karen. "It's the boy from the plane."

"What boy from what plane?" asked Rachel.

"The boy with the iPhone."

Player One

Many things will happen next, and these things will happen quickly, because time does flood, and time also burns, and during this burning flood, Karen will know the world has changed for good. She will sit with the boy from the plane and Luke, and she will think about Casey and her family and she will know that something far greater than 9/11 has occurred — the entire world has now turned into the Twin Towers, and it will never feel normal ever again — and that, in itself, will be the new normal. And somehow Karen will be at peace with this — but not now, for other things must happen, and they must happen quickly. Time speeds up, time speeds down, always time, always rattling our cages, taunting us with our never-ending awareness of its presence, our only weapon against time being our free will and our belief that life is sacred and our hope that we have souls.

And that's when Rick will remember he'd been drinking earlier on, that he'd slipped and lost his sobriety — and then he will wonder if everything now happening to him is just a slip-dream, not reality — wouldn't that explain everything! — and so he'll whack himself on the head, trying to wake himself up, but he won't wake up, and he'll know this isn't a dream.

He'll shout, "I'm cursed! We're all of us cursed!"

Luke will tell him to calm down, but Rick won't. And the blood on the floor in front of him will remind him of high school biology classes. He'll remember that all those mammalian embryos look the same until a certain point in their development, but then somewhere down the line human beings become damned. Are other mammals cursed? What makes humans unique? Our ability to experience time? Our ability to sequence our lives? Our free will? What single final Russian roulette gene sequence condemns us all? We're so close to other animals, and yet we're so utterly different.

Rick will think, *The universe is so large, and the world is so glorious, but here I am with chilled black oil pumping through my veins, and I feel like the unholiest thing on earth.*

"We're all born lost," Rick will say, and Luke will reply, "I don't have an answer to that."

Luke will survey the remains of the day strewn about the lounge, and as he does, he'll be unsure what to do. *Should I pray? I'm no longer convinced I have a soul.*

Then Luke will get paranoid. He will wonder if God is using him. Then he will think, *Well, faith or not, in the end, we are still judged by our deeds, not our wishes. We are the sum of our decisions, and with decisions so often comes sorrow.*

Luke accepts Karen's hand — a hand that cares, a hand that can mould his inner life, a hand that will touch his face and make him see the truth. With her, he will realize that everyone on earth is damaged goods. And *that* is the wonder of it all.

This is when Rachel will have a vision. It won't be a dream or a hallucination — it will be a real vision, more

real than real, actually, as clear and bright and dust-free
as an online second world, and the vision will be this:
Rachel will be crawling through the empty-streeted
remains of the suburb in which she grew up. It will
be the middle of the day, but suddenly the sky will go
black, but not eclipse black. Rather, as occurred in the
candlelit bar, the optical sensation will be more as if the
sun has simply gone out. And yet the sun will still be
above, yet it will be casting no light, not even like a full
moon. The big black sun will be shining down in the
middle of the night. And beneath this dead sun, Rachel
will see cars stopped in mid-journey, their drivers gone.
The front doors of homes will be open, and she knows
that were she to walk into these houses, meals would
be sitting on the table, some still warm, yet there will
never be people coming back to eat them. Some TV sets
might still be on, yet were she to change channels, all
the scenes would be devoid of people — the sitcom
living rooms, the football stadiums, and the six o'clock
news stations — nobody there.

And amid this switched-off landscape, Rachel will
find herself breathing hard, and blood will be pounding
within her head, and she will be shouting to anybody
who will listen, "Awake! Awake! I come to bear good
news! Anyone who can listen, awake! Awaken! Our
time has come. You are thirsty! You are starving! And
you ache to rebuild from the ashes of the present. And
my news is this — hallelujah, we are ready to enter the
Third Testament. Our time has come. Now we move

onward. Fiction and reality have married. What we have made now exceeds what we are. Now is the time to erase the souls we damaged as we crawled down the twentieth century's plastic radiant way. Listen to me! We will soon be reborn. Heed my words, I beg you, as now my vision is coming to an end. Awake! Awake! This is Rachel saying goodbye to you all!"

THE VIEW FROM INSIDE DAFFY DUCK'S HOLE

Karen

The teenage boy enters the candlelit lounge screaming, "My eyes! Rinse my eyes! Oh, God, my *eyes*." Karen half pushes, half yanks him towards the bar, where Rick grabs a pitcher of melted ice water and sluices it over the boy's face. The boy shouts, "I can barely see . . . I *can't* see."

"Hang on," says Karen. "Rick, is there any kind of hose back there?"

"No, just this." Rick aims the five-variety soda nozzle at the boy's face, using its cold, clean pressure to rinse visible chemical fragments from the boy's skin. Meanwhile, Luke continues to guard Bertis.

Karen sees Rachel taping the tablecloths back over the lounge door. She hasn't bothered to barricade it again, and Karen understands why — she had the same thought herself: *What if another innocent needs help? We need to be able to let people in quickly.* Helping others trumps protecting themselves. The barricade has become a liability rather than a necessity; all they need now is an airtight barrier against chemicals.

Karen asks, "What's your name?"

"It's Max. My lips . . . my lips are stinging."

"Oh Jesus. Max, honey, hang in there, okay?"

Karen is having a flashback to five years ago, when Casey had antibiotic-resistant *E. coli* poisoning. The craziness, the hospital, the sadness, and, oh, the helplessness.

Rachel heads behind the bar and turns on the tap, but no water emerges. In her toneless voice she says, "The water isn't working. Max, I want you to remove your clothes. Right now. Drop them on the ground — don't throw them, don't kick up any dust. Then we're going to take you out to the back area and rinse your body with whatever we can find. Nobody touch Max's clothes. We'll bag them later. Karen and Rick, you rinse your hands now with whatever you can find."

While Rick hoses down Karen's forearms, Bertis calls from the floor, "Excuse me, I never got the royal treatment like this guy," to which Karen says, "No. You didn't."

Rachel looks in her purse and removes a prescription container, from which she takes some pills and puts them in Max's hand. "Take these."

"What are they?"

"Propanolol. It's a beta blocker that curtails adrenaline production, which in turn reduces memory production, which in turn reduces post-traumatic stress."

Rick says, "What?" looking at Rachel as if she were a grizzly bear riding a unicycle.

Rachel continues, "The hippocampus loses its ability to make memories adhere to the brain. Guys fighting in Iraq take it all the time. I keep them in case I have a too-big freakout in public."

Rick says, "Are they safe?"

"They are."

Max pops the pills in his mouth and swallows them, and Rick hoses out Max's mouth with what remains from the soda pump. Max continues disrobing as best he can, though his movements are awkward thanks to adrenaline and fear. Karen sees deep, anthrax lesions on his arms and legs. When his cargo shorts hit the ground, she hears a thud. She's guessing that in a pocket of those shorts is the iPhone holding pictures of her taken on the plane what feels like a lifetime ago but was really just earlier that day. For Karen, that thud marks the official start of the rest of her life, and of a whole new way of life — a new world that exists within a state of permanent power failure. A perpetual Lagos, a never-ending Darfur. A world where people eat fortune cookies without bothering to read the fortunes. A world where individuality means little: People are simply Scrabble tiles with no letters, Styrofoam packing peanuts, napkins at McDonald's.

Karen decides that at the first opportunity, she's going to ask Rachel for a few of those pills. Just last month, in the break room with Dr. Yamato, Karen joked that the smartest thing science could do would be to make a pill called September 10; if you took it, it would be as if 9/11 had never happened. Now Karen wants a pill that will make the whole twenty-first century disappear — that will make this unavoidable future vanish. Dr. Yamato said that earth was not built for six billion people, all running around and being passionate about being alive. Earth was built for about two million people foraging for roots and grubs.

"Aren't you being a charmer," Karen said, packing up her cubicle for the day.

Dr. Yamato, crabby after a three-day bipolar symposium, went on, saying, "Karen, history may well prove worthless in the end. Individualism may prove to be only a cruel and unnecessary hoax played on billions of people for no known reason — a bad idea dreamed up by God on the Eighth Day."

Karen had laughed — laughed!

Rick takes over guard duty, and Luke and Karen escort a limping Max to the storage room, over by the recycling bins.

Karen asks, "Where were you when the explosions happened? How did you get here? Were you with your family? Where are they if you're here?"

Max stands in his boxer shorts and says, "We were in a rental car headed downtown."

Luke says, "There's no bottled water or club soda here. The best I can do is melted ice from the machine."

"Do it."

Karen reboots the conversation. "Your family was in the rental car."

"Headed downtown. Me. My dad. My sister."

"Where's your mother?"

"She moved in with her trainer last year. I don't know."

"Sorry."

"It's no big deal. So, we were the last car out of the lot before they stopped renting. The guys at the counter were making weird faces. I looked at their monitors, and there was an override message saying STOP ALL REFUELLING IMMEDIATELY and then STOP ALL NEW RENTALS IMMEDIATELY. *Ouch!*" The melted ice water smells like Teflon and nickels and dimes as it flows over Max's scalp, then dribbles down his torso. "It feels like my entire body's been stung by hornets." A tear forms in his right eye, clearly visible against his angry crimson skin.

Luke grabs a bottle of vodka, pours some into a plastic cup, and adds some Coke to it, then places the cup in Max's hands. "Drink that."

"What then?" asks Karen.

"We didn't get very far. The police began to barricade all the highway routes to the airport. People everywhere were freaking out, and, like, ten thousand people were trying to get back to the airport to fly home. But, I mean, all the flights were stopped — what were they thinking? There's no gas anymore. And then suddenly this guy came and pointed a gun at us, and his buddy started siphoning the gas out of our car. There were a couple of cops nearby and they didn't do anything. This guy just stood there holding a gun, and the other guy drained the tank, and then he made my dad drop the car keys into the gas tank so we couldn't get away driving on what gas remained."

Luke gently lifts Max's left arm and rinses it with the melted ice water.

Karen asks, "What did you do then?"

"That's when the explosions happened."

"What were they?"

"I don't know. Nobody does. We saw that the fallout was headed our way, so we tried to run away from it, but it kept changing course and was on top of us by the time we got to this hotel."

"Was there no other place to go to for safety?"

"What — like under an overpass? No way. That stuff is pure chemical. I tried going into the hotel, but it's locked. Why would they do that?"

Luke and Karen swap glances.

"Where are your father and sister?" Luke says.

"I don't know. We got separated. We couldn't see — from the fogginess of the chemicals and then because our eyes stopped working. And the air was so thick. There was no echo, like in a storm. I — I have no idea where they are." Max begins to cry, and he says to Karen, "I know you. You're that pretty lady from the plane. I recognized you when I first came in, even with only a little bit of eyesight."

Rachel comes in with a bottle and a fresh candle. "I found some more water. I'll keep looking." Rachel leaves and Luke says, "Max, I'm going to rinse as much as I can off you."

"Okay."

Karen looks around as Luke drizzles water over Max. She notices that Rick keeps extra bartender outfits hanging back here. "Try on this shirt," she says, wrapping Max's hand around it. "You're shivering."

"Thanks," he said. "I'm cold."

Max manages to put on the shirt, but the pants sting his raw skin and he cries out. Karen sits on a crate and says, "Max, come and sit beside me. Luke, go fetch the iPhone from Max's cargo pants." Max puts his arms around Karen's neck.

———

Karen remembered holding Casey in the hospital five years ago, the first time she'd held her since she was maybe five or six. Holding her child felt nice. Children have weight. They're warm. You can feel their heart and lungs pumping from within.

Now Max asked, "Am I going to be blind forever?"

Karen said, "No, sweetie, your eyes will be fine. And soon all of this will be over and you'll be home."

Max sat beside Karen, his head slumped and resting on her chest. He was a big kid, not fully grown but almost there.

"I didn't mean what I said earlier."

"What do you mean?"

"That bit about not caring about my mother. Because I do."

"I know you do, Max."

"She just left us. How can someone do that — just leave you, like you're nothing to them?"

"People do it all the time. It's the dark side of people."

"I miss her all the time, and she won't even answer my emails. She pretends she doesn't know how to work a Gmail account. And then she accidentally cc'ed me about a barbecue she was having the afternoon she was supposed to be at my sister's violin recital."

"Violin recital? My daughter plays the violin."

"Really?"

"Yeah. She's fifteen and going through a goth phase right now. I was worried she'd stop going to lessons because it wasn't cool or something."

"I don't get the goth thing."

"I don't, either. When I was her age, you had only two choices: popular or unpopular. There are so many things you can be these days."

"What's your name?"

"I'm Karen."

"My skin hurts, Karen."

Karen almost burst into tears but stopped herself and said, "So, Max, yesterday I went into Subway and bought a sandwich that was totally different from the one I'd normally get. Different toppings, bread, condiments. I got chili peppers and cucumber slices."

"Yeah, and?"

"And then when I went to eat it . . ."

"What?"

"It tasted like somebody else's sandwich."

Max smiled. "That's funny."

"So tell me, Max, why is it that chickens don't taste like eggs? And why is it that traffic lights are red and green but don't seem the least bit Christmassy?"

Max chuckled.

"I'm a bit drunk. Is this gin I'm drinking?"

"It's vodka."

"I've been drunk before."

"Have you, now?"

"I got bed spins. I hated it. Crème de menthe and rye in my friend Jordan's basement. But now is different. You know what I wanted?"

"What do you mean, 'What I wanted'?"

"To do before I die."

"Max, you don't need to think that way."

"I wanted to get shot."

"You *what?*"

"I wanted to get shot. And survive. And what I wanted to do after getting shot was to get my driver's licence and then buy a car, a real wreck from the 1990s, and shoot some holes in its side, because that would be the coolest thing you could ever have on a car. You'd be instantly cooler than if you had a Mustang or Lamborghini." Max's face was lit up as though he were six and Karen had allowed him to lick chocolate cake batter from a pair of electric beaters.

"I'm drunk," Max said.

"You are."

"My body is on fire."

"I'm sorry, sweetie. It'll get better."

"I don't know where my father and sister are."

"I don't know where my daughter is, but I know she'll be okay. You can't worry that way."

Luke came back in. "Here's the iPhone."

"Hand it to me, Luke." Karen looked at the iPhone. "My boss has this same model. Why don't I look at some of your pictures, Max?"

"I can't see them."

"That's okay. I'll look at the pictures and ask questions, and you can fill me in."

"Okay."

Karen fiddled with the screen until she managed to bring up a photo of Max's father and sister at an airport gate. "You're at the airport. Where are you from, Max?"

"Calgary."

Karen scrolled ahead. "What's your sister's name?"

"Heather. A real eighties name. My mother likes it."

A few shots later Karen came to the photos of herself — two taken without her knowledge, the third of her flipping young Max the bird. "And then we come to . . ."

"You found the photos of you, huh?"

"Yes, I did." That last photo was just as funny as Karen had imagined it would be. She smiled. She could sense Luke standing behind her. He had said almost nothing the entire time they'd been in the storage room, but his presence had been strong. She hadn't felt so reassured by another person since her wedding.

Max said, "Hold your breath."

"Huh? Hold my breath?" Karen asked. "Why?"

"Just do it. Please?"

Karen held her breath, and so did Max.

Max said, "You know, I bet if we froze right here and didn't move and didn't breathe, we could stop time from moving forward forever."

"Is that what you think?"

"I do."

Karen looked at Luke, who gestured, *Why not?* He sat down beside her and took her hand, and the three of them sat there, not breathing, frozen in mid-motion, trying to stop time. And for an infinitely thin moment, time did stop. *Heck,* thought Karen, *time could be starting and stopping all the time, and we'd never be the wiser because we are so utterly time's prisoners. In the time it took to think these words, time might have stopped for a billion years. How will we ever know it didn't?*

Karen looked at Luke. Their eyes locked, and Karen knew then that the two of them were connected forever. And then the candle went out, and the room became as dark as the air between two bedsheets.

Rick

Rachel — beautiful, glowing Rachel — returns from delivering water and a candle to Karen, Luke, and Max. She scouts the bar for more water. Rick stands guard over Bertis, duct-taped to his chair and lying on the floor, staring up at a ceiling flecked with scotch-taped holiday tinsel remnants. He croaks to Rick, "So, you scored yourself a bit of afternoon delight, huh?"

"You be quiet. Soon enough you'll be rotting in prison, and after you die you'll reincarnate as a prisoner."

"The world is prison enough already. And reincarnation is a sham. Could I perhaps have a glass of water?"

"There's no water."

"Whatever you have, then. And how come you aren't out back, helping to rinse off Richie Cunningham?"

"I'm watching out for *you*. Guaranteed, with someone like you, I stop paying attention for even ten seconds and you escape like Hannibal Lecter and do God knows what."

"You spoke of God . . ."

From the bar, Rachel says, "I'll get you something to drink. I'm happy to."

This offer surprises Rick, but then Rachel is one big unpredictable quirk. Lovestruck Rick plays in his head a mental preview of his life with Rachel: vacations in Kentucky, purchasing white mouse studs; evenings beside a crackling fireplace, listening to Rachel recite pi out loud; perhaps one of those hug machines for whenever human contact is too much for her brain to handle. Rick foresees an odd, unexpected new life, and he decides that Rachel fetching a beverage for a maimed sniper is simply part of that unexpectedness. So he doesn't protest.

Rachel busies herself behind the bar, setting three glasses on the counter, filling them with flat Coke, mostly syrup. Seeing Bertis's rifle still lying on the bar in a pile of bar-mix crumbs, she picks it up and says, "My father once had a rifle similar to this."

"Don't mess with my rifle!" shouts Bertis.

Rachel walks around the bar to the table that holds the duffle bag and zips the rifle inside.

From the floor, Bertis makes his summons: "Rachel, my beverage, please."

Rachel fetches two glasses of Coke and a spoon, hands one to Rick, then bends down over Bertis to meticulously dole out measured sips of Coke with the teaspoon, as though she were doing a chemistry experiment. Bertis is thirsty and stays silent until his glass is empty, when he says, "Never in my life have I felt more like a white mouse in a lab."

At the mention of white mice, Rachel perks up. "Really? What does it feel like?"

"Huh?"

"What does it feel like to be a white mouse? I've tried to guess, but empathizing with humans is hard enough. I love my white mice, but I don't know how they actually feel. So you can tell me. This is almost better than starting to believe in God."

Bertis calls to Rick, "Buddy, what planet is she from?"

"Answer her question."

"You two are crazy."

"We're not crazy," Rachel says. "I breed white mice for a living."

"You're a teenager dressed like Nancy Reagan."

"I'm dressed like a fertile woman of child-bearing age. And judging by your raised voice, you are either angry or telling a joke." Rachel heads back to the bar and washes her hands with Purell and a bar towel.

Bertis says, "This isn't happening."

"Bertis, can we please discuss white mice?" Rachel says, taking a sip of her Coke.

Rick snickers. "Now you know how we feel when you get all Goddy on us."

Bertis changes the subject. "Rick, would you please untape my hands?"

"What? You can't be serious."

"I am. I have no circulation in them. They don't even feel like hands anymore. Look at them. They're white. I'm not asking you something major. Handcuff me to the table, if you like. There are cuffs in the inside pocket of my bag. But I need more blood circulation. And may I remind you that your buddy shot off my toe?"

"There are cuffs in your bag? How did I miss those? Wait — why do you have cuffs in your bag?"

"When I set out today on my holy mission, I wasn't sure what the day might . . . *entail*."

Rachel says, "I think it's safe, Rick. You hold the gun

to his head while I cut the duct tape on his wrists, then cuff him to the table."

"Fine. Let's do it."

Rachel opens the bag and locates the cuffs, then kneels on the floor beside Bertis. Rick watches closely, holding his shotgun to Bertis's head as the duct tape binding his hands is sliced off. Then Rachel slides the table closer and cuffs Bertis's right arm to one of the legs. The transition occurs without incident.

"There. I can move my hands. Thank you."

"Jesus, all of this craziness, just because oil implodes," says Rick.

"Oil is black and thick like sludge, Rick — like the unsaved blood that pumps through your heart."

"Okay, Bertis," says Rick. "I guess we're overdue for a sermon. Go on, then. I'm all ears."

Truth be told, Rick likes the way Bertis speaks. It's a lot like the way Leslie Freemont spoke, except with a different sales pitch. He likes the sound and the flow of the words.

Bertis says, "There is no middle ground between belief and non-belief, Rick, no shades, no mid-tones. Surrender all of your logic and theories to blind faith. What is written is true. My words contain no errors, and a man who spreads the word is holy and must be obeyed. And Rick, there is so much you need to learn. For example, men and women are two different animals and must be treated as such. And now that the Apocalypse has happened, more than ever you must accept belief. You must

learn to attack moderates — those people who think
a middle ground can exist — and feel pity and disgust
for people who believe in a cartoon world of peace and
love — it only makes them easier to kill. You must choose
between death and becoming someone entirely new."

"And how will that feel?"

"It will feel, Rick, as if you died and were reincarnated,
yet stayed inside your own body."

"You said reincarnation was a sham."

"Shush. Your new life will be coloured and perfumed
by the sensation of imminent truth. Change your name if
you like. Sever all links to the previous world. Disappear
from the world completely for months and months. Let
those in your life give you up for dead. Let the remains
of your former existence be an uninterpreted dream. But
remember, you will soon be different, and there aren't
enough words for 'transform.' No more excuses for you,
Rick: no drugs, no sleeping, no booze, no overworking,
no repetition or insulation or efforts to make time disappear. You're in for the long haul. Can you do that, Rick?"

"I —" Rick stops for a second. "What's with the way
you talk?"

Bertis is genuinely taken aback. "What?"

"The way you talk. Aside from the subject matter, it
feels like it's coming from some different place, or some
other part of history. Did you study how to talk like that?
Do they teach that in schools — how to talk weird?"

Rachel says, "Bertis is being poetic, Rick. He uses
rhythm and regularity of speech to make you forget

about yourself so that his words will have a stronger impact. We were taught to recognize poetry in normalcy training. It's like music — it's a powerful way to quickly and effectively indoctrinate normals."

Rick thinks this over, smiles at his sweetheart, and says, "Let me guess, Rachel — you don't understand music either, do you?"

"No," replies Rachel. "Much of what normal people think of as art is simply the establishment of repetitive structures that become interesting when they are broken in certain ways."

Bertis says, "That's not true, Rachel. Is that all your new relationship to God is — a pattern to be broken?"

"It's a bit new to me. I haven't thought it through yet."

"You're already in God's house, Rachel. Now it's just a matter of locating your room."

Rick says, "Get real, Bertis. Humans are part of nature, and nature is one great big wood chipper. Sooner or later, everything shoots out the other end in a spray of blood, bones, and hair."

"No!" shouts Bertis. "That is not true. We are beasts, yet we are divine. We have apprehension. We can ask questions."

"I thought it was all about believing *without* questioning."

"*Ahhh* . . . arrogance. Man's curse. Just you watch, Rick — the world makes cat food out of people who think like you."

"What should I be doing, then?"

"You should be accepting faith, Rick. You should be spreading the good word. You should be etching the good word onto the glass scanning beds of library photocopiers. You should be scraping the truth onto old auto parts and throwing them off bridges so that people digging in the mud in a million years will question the world, too. You should be carving eyeballs into tire treads and onto shoe soles so that your every trail speaks of thinking and faith and belief. You should be designing molecules that crystallize into poems of devotion. You should be making bar codes that print out truth, not lies. You shouldn't even throw away a piece of litter unless it has the truth stamped on it — a demand for people to reach a finer place!"

Rick is enjoying Bertis's words — not even because of their content, but because he likes their pattern, their Leslie Freemontishness.

Bertis continues: "Rick, your new life will be tinged with urgency, as though you're digging out the victims of an avalanche. If you're not spending every waking moment of your life living the truth, if you're not plotting every moment to boil the carcass of the old order, then you're wasting your day."

"Wow," says Rick. "That spiel is better than what Leslie Freemont offers."

"That *Antichrist*. That *demon*."

During Bertis's speech, Rachel has been studying his hands and fingers and his Medic-Alert bracelet, and she suddenly makes a connection. "You have spatulate fingernails."

"Huh? So what?"

"You're Leslie Freemont's son, aren't you? And I'm guessing that Tara used to be your wife."

Bertis spits, "You *witch*!" just as Luke, Karen, and Max enter the room, asking if they've found more water.

In one smooth act of choreography, Bertis yanks the tablecloth off the table with his left hand, pulls over the duffle bag, and sets it on his lap. Within a second he has the rifle out of the bag, his right hand on the trigger, and the barrel pointing at Rachel. The bullet hits her chest, and a drop of her blood lands in Rick's eye.

———

Rick ran to Rachel and wrapped his arms around her. Luke ran over and jumped on top of Bertis, whose face was swelling. He seemed to be having a seizure. Bertis hissed his last words at Luke and Rick — "*God owns everything*" — while Luke shouted, "What the hell's happening out here?"

Rachel looked at Bertis and said, "Peanut allergy."

"*What?* How could you know that?"

"His father had it. He said so when he was here. I put peanut dust all over the rifle, just in case," then her legs buckled, and Rick, assisted by Karen, eased her to the floor. Luke looked at the rifle's trigger, which was covered in powdered bar mix. "God, what a screwed-up world," he said.

Rick's heart lay smashed on the floor like an egg. His

sense of time had gone AWOL. He didn't feel old or young or asleep or dreaming or awake. He was living his whole life inside this one moment. His brain sizzled with hormones and enzymes and misfiring electrical sparks — it was amazing that he could even remember who he was. He probed Rachel's wound and felt the bullet lodged in her bone. He had the feeling that if he reached deeper into her body he could remove gold coins and keys and tropical birds and diamonds. He thought about the blood flowing through his veins and through Rachel's. Was her heart beating? Was she cooling off as he sat there with her in his arms?

Luke came over and said, "I'll make a bandage. I'll tie these napkins together."

Rick took the napkins from Luke and held them against Rachel's wound. He thought, *We're all born separated from God — over and over, life makes sure to let us know this — and yet we're all real. We have names. We have stories. We mean something. We must. But what if my life is a badly told story? Maybe a badly told story only serves to remind us that there is no life after death.*

Karen handed Rick a busing tray filled with melted ice and Rick sucked in a gulp of air as he rinsed away the worst of the blood from Rachel's chest. *Now I know for sure that hate is going to enter my life. I can feel it multiplying within me like a rapidly doubling zygote. And even if I eventually shed that ever-growing hate, let it drop from me like a chunk of concrete — what will fill the hole it leaves? The universe is so large, and the world is so glorious, but here I am with chilled black oil pumping through my veins, and I feel like the unholiest thing on earth.*

Luke

Luke is sitting with Karen and trying to remember what day of the week it is. *This almost feels like an extravagance from an already-vanished era when knowing the day of the week might somehow have mattered.* He asks Karen, "Is it a Tuesday? Was it Wednesday? Will it soon be Thursday? I can't remember."

"I can't either, Luke."

It feels to Luke like a generic day — or rather, it feels how days must have felt before the seven days of the week were invented. He wonders if the builders of Stonehenge felt this same sense of daylessness. Except with Stonehenge, they probably felt yearlessness and wanted some form of confirmation that the year was about to change, that their winters would end.

Bertis is dead, his corpse dragged out back. Max is resting on a raft of tablecloths; candles light him as he lies still, moaning occasionally. Rachel is alive, but barely, also on a raft of tablecloths, and Rick is by her side, morose and speechless. In the candlelight the blood covering his shirt makes it seem like it is made of Plasticine.

So Luke is sitting with Karen, monitoring Max's and Rachel's conditions, giving Max occasional sips of water they discovered in a concealed tray beneath the ice machine.

Outside the cocktail lounge, the chemical dust is still kicking around and Warren is but a fluffy pink speed bump. Until the chemicals stop falling, everybody is going to be marooned in the lounge. Luke tried to go for help, running across the breezeway to the hotel doors, but now they were not only locked as before but barricaded, too. And then, back in the cocktail lounge, he had to strip down like Max and rinse himself off, so now he's wearing one of Rick's spare bartender outfits.

Luke knows that technically he ought to be drunk, but he stopped feeling drunk hours ago. He feels super-clear now. He can see everything. And in his mind he's thinking of a pair of bar magnets he stole decades ago from the high school storeroom, magnets that travelled with him across his life, always stashed in the drawer of his bedside tables alongside a Bible. Luke kept these magnets because he could never figure out why north attracts south and why similar poles repel, but he thought if he looked closely enough, he might see threads hurling themselves across space, fighting each other — visibly fighting each other. In his early twenties he still had the bar magnets, and he asked his older sister, a radiologist, how magnets communicated with each other to either attract or repel. She said, "They have fields around them."

"Okay, but what's a field?"

"A field is what surrounds a magnet."

"That's a non-answer. How does a field work?"

"Well, we know how to work with fields, to predict how strong they'll be, how to manipulate them with, say, motion inside of dams, or with particle accelerators."

"That's not my question. What I want to know is, are

there little electrons down there, like tiny little M&M candy guys wearing boxing gloves, hovering around their poles, duking it out?"

"No, fields don't operate with particles."

"So how do they operate?"

"We don't know."

"We don't know?"

"We don't."

"So all we know about fields is that they exist."

"Pretty much. They warp space. You just have to accept that fields are fields, and we'll probably never understand how they do it. Gravity is a field, too. It does the same thing, except it's way weaker. It takes a planet the size of earth to generate enough gravitational field to make a rock fall down. One good small magnet can have just as much attractive power."

"I see."

But Luke didn't see. It continued to bother him. *If we don't know what a field is, what else will we never be able to understand? And what other fields exist that are either too big or too small to appreciate on the human level?*

Karen says, "I'm sorry about your father. My mother is going through the same thing right now. Alzheimer's."

"Huh." Luke thinks a bit. "I used to think Alzheimer's was a punishment sent to us as a species for refusing to change our ways." He pauses a beat. "I hope that didn't sound preachy."

"You mean, refusing to change our ways as individuals?"

"Individually, collectively. I've learned over the years that people almost never change. The crap I used to hear from my flock. Most people learn nothing from life. Or if they do, they conveniently forget what they've learned when it suits their needs. Most people, given a second chance, screw it up royally. It's one of those laws of the universe you can't shake. *Maybe* they learn something once they get their third chance — after wasting vast sums of time, money, youth, energy. But even if they learn something, it doesn't mean they're going to change their lives. Most of them simply become bitter because they never had the strength of spirit to make bold strokes."

"You probably heard a lot of problems in your line of work."

"I did. Tell me, has your mother . . . has she forgotten you yet?"

"Yes. Did your father forget you?"

"Yeah. Almost immediately."

Karen says, "My mom's sort of turning into an animal now, but I don't know what kind of animal. She screeches. She makes lowing noises. She has stopped being human. It makes me wonder what it means to be human, as opposed to being something else. But at the same time, I no longer think humans are stuck with our natures the way a dog wants bones or a cat wants to chase mice. There's a weird kind of hope that comes from that. We *can* change into something else, even if it's something we don't understand."

"Hmmm," says Luke. "My battle is trying to decide whether it's worth making memories if in the end I'm just going to lose them all, through disease or death. What's the point of it all if I'm just going to go gaga?"

"I hate that expression," says Karen.

"Sorry."

"No, it's okay. The doctors I work for actually use that word every day in the lunchroom. But I still don't like it."

Max opens his mouth and gestures for a sip of water, which Karen gives him.

Luke says, "Well, time does erase both the best and the worst of us." He looks around. "Aren't *we* being cheerful?"

They both scan the room and, perversely, laugh — first a giggle, then a nervous gut crunch. Rick looks up, confused, and Luke finally composes himself and says, "Oh man. We're a disaster of a species, aren't we? People, I mean."

Rick croaks, "Are we?"

Luke says, "We completely *are*. I'm not even going to single out human beings as the Number One disaster on this planet — I'm going to single out our *DNA* as the criminal. Our DNA is a disaster. Everything we make is the fault of our evil little DNA molecule. *Hi, I'm a little DNA molecule. I build cathedrals and go to the moon — heck, I harnessed atomic energy! Take that, viruses.*" Luke looks around the room. "And this is what it gets us in the end. Bar mix. Blindness. Toxic snow.

A dead energy grid. Phones that don't work. We're a joke."

The room goes quiet again.

Eventually Karen says, "You know, Luke, there's a good side to forgetting things, too. Like at night, when you're dreaming and dead friends and relatives show up and you don't understand that they're dead — there's something not quite right about them being there, but they're definitely not dead. Imagine what this would have been like a few hundred years ago: if you made it to fifty or sixty, the dead would populate your entire dream life. It must have been much nicer for the dreamer than being awake. Forgetting stuff protects us, too, Luke."

Luke thinks of his own life, pre–oil crash. He once believed that unless a person goes through some Great Experience, that person's life will have been for naught. He comforted himself with the belief that a quiet life of loneliness could be its own Great Experience. He found himself spending half his time inventing things to say that made it okay to be sleeping alone at night. If he's honest, he became a pastor because he thought that advising other people on their problems would negate the fact that he had no life. He came to dread hearing the problems of his flock, yet he yearned to share in the problems of someone he actually loved.

And here sits Karen. Luke wants to hear her problems. And it seems she doesn't mind hearing his. She opens a door. She asks, "Do you have a dog, Luke?"

"A dog. No. Why do you ask?"

"When you're single and over forty, having a dog is good in that it means you can still form bonds and relationships."

"But there's a dark side to that," Luke says.

"There is?"

"Yup. It could mean that you've stopped being able to form connections with other humans."

"Uh-oh. Always a trap door, isn't there?"

"Always."

"I like you, Luke."

"I like you, too, Karen."

"Are you lonely, Luke?"

"Yeah."

"Me too."

The room went quiet. In the distance a siren flared up and down and came and went. Luke said, "I was actually getting to be okay with it — loneliness — but I can't do it anymore."

"Loneliness is what brought me to this ridiculous bar," said Karen. "Is Mother Nature a prankster or what?"

"She is."

"Do you think you'll miss being a preacher?"

"A pastor? No, I doubt it. I'm tired of people believing the first thing that passes by their eardrums. I'm tired of the way we're all hard-wired to believe lies."

"Churches are a lie?"

"There are thousands of them. Some of them have to be wrong. And I don't want to think of myself as someone who's interested only in people who are in pain. I'm not a vampire. I'm not a saint."

"One of the doctors in my office made an observation. He was Irish and super-Catholic. He said that if there were two Catholics left on earth, one of them would have to be Pope."

"Ha! That's good."

"And Luke, what's the deal with meatballs, anyway?"

"Meatballs?"

"Yeah, meatballs. Who do they think they're trying to fool? We all know they're just meatloaf in disguise."

"You have a unique perspective on life, don't you?"

"You have to when you have a fifteen-year-old goth daughter. If you don't, you develop one pretty quick when you're in Safeway and she asks the guy at the butcher counter for a pint of cow's blood."

"How did you react?"

"I kept my cool, thank you. If it wasn't cow's blood, it would have been something else. A flame-thrower. A pneumatic staple gun. When she went through her vegetarian phase, I bought her tofu hot dogs and she gave me this lecture on how vegetarian hot dogs were, technically, more offensive than hot dogs made from meat by-products."

"How so?"

"She said it was using a way of life based on peace and joy to recreate the worst possible dimension of meat. She said it was like trying to make non-Nazi Nazis."

"That's funny." He paused. "Hey, you know another thing I've been thinking about the church? It's two things, really."

"What?"

"I was watching the marching band at the school down the street practise on the field, and they were just *appalling* — a smoking-trainwreck version of Fleetwood Mac's 'Don't Stop Thinking About Tomorrow,' or whatever the song is called — and the old guy who takes care of the equipment was standing beside me watching and he said, 'Ah, the young angels. You know the secret of marching bands, don't you?' I said I didn't and he said, 'It's simple. Even if half of the students are playing random musical notes, it still sounds like they're a coordinated band.' And that's kind of how I feel about organized anything, including religion."

"You said there were two things about the church."

"You're right. Last month I was buying some green plates in the Chinese store, to replace the ones that got chipped in day-to-day use, and I couldn't find the ones I usually buy. I asked the owner if they were out of production, and he smiled and said, 'They've been in production for four hundred years, and they'll still be in production in another four hundred. And the stack is over by the window now.' I guess I don't want to be just another green plate, replaceable, identical, and forgotten."

"Luke, feeling unique and being unique aren't the same thing."

"I know. But still. We have to *count*. I want to be part

of history. I want a Wikipedia page. I want Google hits. I don't want to be just a living organism that comes and goes and leaves no trace on this planet."

"And what's wrong with that?"

This was a question Luke had no answer for, but he didn't have to answer because just then the power came back on and a space that had felt like a medieval painting now felt like a crime scene photo. The horror of the past few hours, frozen like a tableau in a natural history museum: creatures of the Paleozoic era; Conestoga wagons crossing the prairies, shedding pianos and armoires along the way; the International Space Station growing bean sprouts in zero gravity; a cocktail lounge in the middle of the North American continent filled with blood and guns and twisted bodies and scattered bar mix, a testament to the carnage and disaster that befell humanity the moment the oil ran out. Karen sat cradling Max, her psyche held together with Scotch tape and rubber bands, saying nothing that might further trouble the blind boy. Rick sat silent and furious as he held the perfect Rachel, genetically advanced or genetically flawed, depending on how you looked at her soon-to-vanish being.

Life is short, Luke thought. *And fate is for losers. And money is almost certainly a crystallization of time and free will — but it needs sweet crude oil to survive.*

Luke continued surveying the remains of the day, unsure what to do. His faith was gone, but more than ever he remained convinced he possessed a soul — because his soul had experienced the past five hours and the pain and love it felt — but then, what good was a soul without faith?

Karen was in tears and Luke took her hand. In doing so, he accepted the sorrow of the human condition. Luke knew that this was the moment his father would have stated, "This is all God's doing." And then he would have turned to Luke and said, "And now, son, would be a good time for a prayer."

Rachel/Player One

This is Rachel, a.k.a. Player One. I'm no longer with you, but I'm not in pain or anything, so please don't worry. I finally get to see what exists down inside that black cartoon hole Daffy Duck used to slap onto the ground to get himself out of trouble. The birds are here with me now, and so are the plants and all of God's fine animals. I'm sitting in a glade, with all the creatures in the forest sitting around me, a dove on my left palm and a grey squirrel on my right. I am dozing, resting, feeling completely at peace. Stillness is what I have here — wherever here is. I'm no longer a part of the world, but I'm not yet a part of what follows.

I don't know how long I'll be here. This is a stopping point only, and you'd think I'd be bored here, but boredom exists only in linear time. Eternity isn't linear, so there's no boredom. No current events, either. Eternity is free of news because there's no timeline. It's everything and nothing. No calendars inside Eternity.

It is cooler here, too, and quiet. And I don't look at things the same way anymore, because — well, guess what — I now understand metaphors! That's a surprise. I know that one thing *can* be something else. A burning book indeed equals fascism. Gently cooing doves equal peace. In my ears I hear a noise, and that noise is the sound of the colour of the sun. That's like four metaphors wrapped up into one! Anything can be anything!

I don't think my child — if that's what it was when I was shot, my fertilized DNA clump — is here with me. But I'm not sad, because the DNA clump is probably in a here of its own.

I have mostly happy memories of being alive on earth. I remember how shampoo foam circling the bathtub drain resembles galaxies. I remember my father driving around the block three times so I could hear the whole version of Buddy Holly's "Everyday" on the radio. I remember being allowed to stay home from school to reprogram the coffee maker to display European time instead of North American time. And I remember the bathroom steaming up and my mother's handwriting appearing as if by magic on the foggy mirror: the words "I ♥ Rachel." I didn't know what that meant — why would someone mix a heart shape with letters? But of course it meant she loves me — hearts equal love! And I know this because of how my heart was beating with Rick. That's a happy memory, too.

Poor Rick. Poor Luke. Poor Karen. Poor Max . . . Poor everybody, really. Humans have to endure everything in life in agonizingly endless clock time — every single second of it. Not only that, but we have to *remember* enduring our entire lives. And then there is the cosmic punchline that our lives are, in fact, minuscule compared to geological time or the time frames of the galaxies and stars.

Dreams help fix the curse and gift of time perception. I wonder if humans are the only animal to know the difference between sleeping and dreaming. Dogs and cats probably don't differentiate too much between dreams and real life. And people probably didn't much either until the past few centuries. Nor did they over-analyze the voices they heard in their heads during the day — they probably didn't even realize that they themselves were creating those voices. They probably thought the voice in their head was the king, or the gods passing in and out like some cosmic late-night AM radio station bouncing off the lower ionosphere, allowing them to hear distant ideas and sounds.

I wonder if my DNA clump is sleeping. Can eggs sleep? Can sperm sleep and dream? They're only half-creatures, really — how can they be alive? And how can they dream? I think the division point between where life begins and ends is far murkier than we might think.

The only other sounds I can hear around me down inside Daffy Duck's hole, other than nature sounds, are prayers and curses; they're the only sounds with the power to cross over to wherever it is I am. Do prayers create electrical fields? Is that how they cross the universe? Who's to say? I have no idea how cellphones connected me to call centres in Mumbai, but they still did it. Poor humanity, praying and cursing and praying and cursing. What is to become of us as a species?

A part of me doesn't worry about us. If we can breed wolves into wiener dogs in ten generations, what might we do with a billion years? Never mind what *God* might do with a billion years. Human existence has been so short. For every person currently alive, there are nineteen dead people who lived before us. That's not that many, really, and maybe our time as a species was only ever meant to be short. Luke is right: Human DNA truly is, in so many ways, a total disaster. I heard him say that just before I came here — or I'm pretty sure it was Luke. He and Rick were both wearing bartender's outfits. I'm a broken record, but why can't people wear name tags?

What would God say about evolution? Why has nobody ever asked that specific question that particular way? God's probably been having a big chuckle since eighteen-fifty-whatever, watching humans scramble and bunker and fight and scream over evolution. God made our DNA, thus God made us. What matters is that He got us here, to this point. Or maybe the DNA did it all. Whether you're a believer or a nonbeliever, it's a win-win scenario.

I think cloning is where it's probably going to get really fun. Imagine being a lab worker in 2050 and creating a great-great-great-grandchild during a coffee break. Or blackmailers holding your hairbrushes hostage, something like, "Give us your money or we'll make ten of you — and then kill them all." Or maybe captains of industry rewriting their wills, deeding everything to themselves down the line, forever and always. And imagine being born and getting an owner's manual written by the previous versions of you — like the manual that comes with a 2011 Volkswagen Jetta. Imagine all the time this would save us — wasted time, hopeless dreams. Maybe this is how we get to evolve forward, electively mutating our way out of our present dire situation — because mutation on its own isn't going to make it happen. Human beings are going to have to speed things up considerably if we're going to survive on this piece of milky blue rock. We need technology, and thank heavens technology is the inevitable result of our freakish DNA. I'm quite certain that intelligent beings on other planets have had growth curves just like ours, and maybe they've mutated forward too, but it's not like aliens are going to come do our hard work for us.

Back when I was young, I used to believe in Superman. He was an alien life form, just like me. I chose to believe I was from some other planet, because if I were, then I wouldn't have to be a "beautiful" girl marooned in a North American suburb at the start of the twenty-first century — a beautiful girl who couldn't tell one person's face from another and who could only sleep covered with ten blankets' worth of weight on top of her, whose father didn't think of her as a real human being, and who would scream if potatoes touched the meat on her plate. Instead, as a space alien like Superman, everything I did would be supernatural and meaningful. Even the smallest of my daily acts would be awe-inspiring and shocking. I remember watching silkworms pupate in science class. Imagine you came from outer space and someone showed you a butterfly and a caterpillar. Would you ever put the two of them together? That was me. But of course, Superman is an anatomical impossibility, and

I've lost my sense of kinship with him, and just who am I now? Sometimes I think humans don't even exist as discrete persons. Rather, there is only the probability of you being *you* at any given moment. While you're healthy, that probability remains pretty high, but when you're sick or old, it shrinks. Your chance of being "all there" becomes less and less. When you have Alzheimer's, like Luke's dad and Karen's mom, the probability of being you drops to almost zero — and then you die, and it really *is* zero — except here I am now, talking, so who's to say?

I'm not being too cheerful, am I? I have to watch it with that sort of thing. I may be in the hereafter, but my normalcy training seems to be sticking. I don't want to give offence to other people. I don't need the trouble. Being different is hard, and being different in the New Normal is going to be harder still.

The New Normal.

You people still on earth are now inhabiting an era in which all human personality characteristics are linked to some form of brain feature. Personality is a slot machine, and the cherries, lemons, and bells are your SSRI system, your schizophrenic tendency, your left/right brain lobalization, your anxiety proclivity, your wiring glitches, your place on the autistic and OCD spectrums — and to these we must add the deep-level influences of the machines and systems of intelligence that guided your brain into maturity. I could go on, but do remember that, in the end, it's real people at the end of all these variables, not androids. And if you don't have the courage to face the truth about how we are made, then you don't deserve the wonder that comes with being alive, regardless of how your particular slot machine generated you. Knowing your demons won't chase away your angels, and you won't be able to kill your demons, so you can't get melodramatic that way.

Of course, nurture is a factor in the slot machine, too, as is your geographical entry point onto planet Earth. But in the New Normal, the effects of geography and nurture will grow fuzzier as the Internet allows collective real-time fulfillment of the needs and dreams of the human species. If we view the brain as a device designed to allow us to experience and foster free will, then we'll see a staggeringly concentrated expression of will occurring with extreme speed. As this happens, the modern economy will stop being about the redistribution of wealth and start being about the redistribution of time and options. Shopping is not creating. We're all stuck on the same airplane flight now, and they just got rid of first class and business class.

Listen to me, metaphoring like crazy. And trying to define time while no longer living inside it. Past, present, and future tenses now seem like party novelties, and keeping my tenses straight here has been difficult. But I do remember a bit of life before the twenty-first century, and I do remember the sensation, especially after 9/11, that time had stopped feeling like time. Society collectively lost the sense that an era feels like an era —

they forgot the way it felt when time and emotions and culture were particular to one spot in time, the way I suppose decades felt in the twentieth century. And lives stopped feeling like lives — or at least, people began talking about not having a life. What could that mean? Information overload triggered a crisis in the way people saw their lives. It sped up the way we locate, cross-reference, and focus the questions that define our essence, our roles — our stories. The crux seems to be that our lives stopped being stories. And if we are no longer to have lives that are stories, what will our lives have become? Yet seeing one's life as a story seems like nostalgic residue from an era when energy was cheap and the notion of the super-special, ultra-important individual with blogs and Google hits and a killer résumé was a conceit the planet was still able to materially support. In the New Normal, we need to strip ourselves of notions of individual importance. Some-thing new is arising that has neither interest in nor pity for souls trapped in twentieth-century solipsism. Non-linear stories? Multiple endings? No loading times? It's called life on earth. Life need not be a story, but it does need to be an adventure.

In a thousand years, electively mutated post-humans will look back at us with awe and wonder. They'll say that this was when humans and the planet got married, fused, melted together, the moment when one could no longer separate the two. I hope they see that we did it with a sense of humour. Yes, I realize from my new perspective that it was ridiculous of me to buy a $3,400 dress to find a mate in a seedy airport cocktail lounge. And yes, it was sweet and funny for Karen to end up on Max's social networking page as a cougar.

But here's the new deal: I just realized I'm being allowed to return to earth — and I'm being allowed to return with my DNA clump, which will become a 6.3-pound baby girl next April. I guess that's why they brought me here to the glade, to sort things out.

And so I'm going to have a future tense.

And so I'm going to have a story.

And many things will soon happen . . .

It will begin to rain, and the chemicals outside the lounge will crackle and fizz and drain away. Gas will be rationed and doled out by the government, and it will never go below $350 a barrel again.

The police will show up and everyone will leave. Karen will live in a hostel with Luke while they wait three weeks for planes to fly again. A few months after that they will get married, and Luke's former flock won't press embezzlement charges and will instead pray for Luke — which makes me think they are a bit stupid. But Karen and Luke and young Casey will have their happy ending.

Rick? Rick will go to the hospital with Max and me. Max will be blind and I'll lose my ability to understand metaphors and humour — I'll miss them very much. I'm not sure if I'll still believe in God. That remains to be seen. But what I can see is that I'll marry Rick, and I'll breed white mice and pay our bills that way. Best of all, my father will think of me as a real human being, which is all this trip was ever really about, and so I get my happy ending, too.

However, I won't be allowed to remember everything I've learned here in the quiet place — which is sad — and I have to leave soon. My final thoughts? Poor humanity! Poor everyone! My poor fellow citizens, children of the children of the children of the pioneers who somehow became immune to God, citizens inhabiting a New Normal world of robotized collective minds that exist everywhere and nowhere. Metaminds with inexplicable biases and wants and unslakeable thirsts — real-time fear all the time. Bertis Freemont wasn't so wrong after all.

And we're all waiting for It now, aren't we? Good old "It" — the It who rains, the It we mean when we ask what time is It? I suppose It is the arrival of the Sentience. The arrival of the metamind that is us and yet much more than us. It is the Sentience that will eclipse us, that will encourage us, and shame us and indulge us. *It* is out there waiting. I'm certainly waiting — it's why I'm here, talking to you before I enter the New Normal, too.

And so before I enter this new world, curiously, the words that come to me are the words of Leslie Freemont, and I raise the hand that holds a sleeping dove and put forth a toast to you all: "Here's a toast to everyone on earth who's ever been eager — no, *desperate* — for even the smallest sign that there exists something finer, larger, and more miraculous about our inner selves than we could ever have supposed. Here's to all of us reaching out our hands to other people everywhere, reaching out to pull them from the icebergs on which they stand frozen, to pull them through the burning hoops of fire that frighten them, to help them climb over the brick walls that block their paths. Let us reach out to shock and captivate people into new ways of thinking."

I have this funny feeling that I wouldn't have missed earth for anything, so I must be getting something out of the experience. I hope you do, too.

I, Rachel, a.k.a. Player One, can now see the nighttime light of your real world.

Good night and goodbye to you all.

Future Legend

Achronogeneritropic Spaces
Nowhere/everywhere/timeless places such as airports.

Airport-Induced Identity Dysphoria
Describes the extent to which modern travel strips the traveller of just enough sense of identity so as to create a need to purchase stickers and gift knick-knacks that bolster their sense of slightly eroded personhood: flags of the world, family crests, school and university merchandise.

Aloneism
A recognition of the fact that it is a burdensome amount of work to be an individual, and also that many human beings were not necessarily cut out to be individuals and are much happier being lost inside a collective environment or a self-denying belief system. Individualism may, in fact, be a form of brain mutation not evenly spread throughout the population, a mutation

that poses a threat to those not possessing it, hence the ongoing war between religion and secularism.

Ambivital Consensus

The fact that there's really no common consensus on where "life" begins, or what is living: cells and bacteria are easy, perhaps, but what about eggs and sperm, which are each only 50 percent of a human, yet seem quite alive? Meanwhile, scientists, still not finished haggling over viruses, have now discovered nanobes, tiny filament structures that some argue represent the smallest living organism yet.

Ameteoric Landscape

Describes the incredibly small extent to which the earth's surface, protected by a thick defensive atmospheric layer, is defined by meteoric impacts compared to its moon, to Mars, and to the solar system's other moons. There have been some minor incidents since the last great meteor, broken into pieces, collided with the earth sixty-five million years ago, killing off the dinosaurs and two-thirds of all life and leaving a number of craters across the planet's surface. That was just the most recent of numerous meteor strikes that caused mass extinctions and drastically altered life on earth over hundreds of millions of years.

Androsolophilia

The state of affairs in which a lonely man is romantically desirable while a lonely woman is not.

Anorthodoxical Isms
The isms that pose the greatest threat to inflexible religious orthodoxies:

Humanism
Cultural Relativism
Moral Relativism
Secularism

The Anthropocene
A term recognizing that human intrusion on the planet's surface and into the atmosphere has been so extreme as to qualify our time on earth as a specific geological epoch. Along with vast increases in anthropogenic emissions of greenhouse gases, which have drastically raised the atmospheric concentration of carbon dioxide, our human footprint now covers more than 83 percent of the earth's surface, according to the Wildlife Conservation Society.

Anthropozooku
Small haiku-like moments during which human and animal behaviours exhibit total overlap.

Antifluke
A situation in the universe in which rigid rules of action exist to prevent coincidences from happening. Given the infinite number of coincidences that could happen, very few ever actually *do*. The universe exists in a coincidence-hating state of antifluke.

Attack-Moderates

The result of a common political tactic used by members of extreme orthodoxies. By forcing people in the political middle to polarize over issues about which they don't feel polar, the desired end state is achieved — one in which the hyperamplification of what was not very much to begin with creates a tone of hysteria amid daily cultural discourse. This resulting hysteria becomes a political tool used by the instigators to push through agendas that would never have been possible in a non-hysterical situation.

Bell's Law of Telephony

No matter what technology is used, your monthly phone bill magically remains about the same size.

Binary Subjective Qualities

Subjective human qualities that most of us take for granted but which remain elusive for some people with brain anomalies. These include humour, empathy, irony, musicality, and a sense of beauty. Subjective sensitivity is often regulated by specific nodes in the right side of the brain that fine-tune and contextualize the information we take in. (See also Cartoon Blindness; Cloud Blindness; Metaphor Blindness)

Blank-Collar Workers

Formerly middle-class workers who will never be middle-class again and who will never come to terms with that.

Capillarigenerative Memory
The tendency of history to remember people who invent new hairstyles: for example, Julius Caesar, Albert Einstein, Marilyn Monroe, Adolf Hitler, and the Beatles.

Cartoon Blindness
A brain connectivity issue that makes a person dislike cartoons or information presented using illustration. Specific versions include an aversion to Saturday morning children's television and the inability to understand and appreciate *New Yorker* cartoons. Seriously.

Catastrophasic Shifts
Enormous, life-changing decisions that are delayed until a crisis has been reached. In most cases this is the worst time to be making such decisions.

Centennial Blindness
The inability of most people to understand future time frames longer than about a hundred years. Many people have its cousin, Decimal Blindness — the inability to think beyond a ten-year time span — and some people have the higher-speed version, Crastinal Blindness — the inability to think past tomorrow.

Christmas-Morning Feeling
A sensation created by stimulus to the anterior amygdala that leaves one with a strong sense of expectation. (See also Godseeking)

Chronocanine Envy
Sadness experienced when one realizes that, unlike one's dog, one cannot live only in the present tense. As Kierkegaard said, "Life must be lived forward." (See also Sequential Thinking)

Chronophasia
An inability to maintain stable circadian rhythms or to approximate time or time sequencing, possibly caused by irregularities in the 20,000-cell region of the brain called the suprachiasmatic nucleus.

Chronotropic Drugs
Drugs engineered to affect one's sense of time. Chrono-decelocotropic drugs have no short-term effect but over time give one the impression that time feels longer. Chronoaccelocotropic drugs have the opposite effect.

Cloud Blindness
The inability of some people to see faces or shapes in clouds. Like prosopagnosia, or "Face Blindness," the cause can be traced to impairment of the fusiform gyrus of the inferior temporal lobe. Fun fact: the psychological phenomenon of seeing faces in clouds or perceiving as significant other vague and random stimuli is called pareidolia.

Collapse Attraction
The situation in which people are usually at their most

attractive and interesting shortly before a total personality collapse. While some of us are attracted to those
who are vulnerable — because it makes us feel good by
comparison, or it makes us feel good to be able to help,
or to *think* we can help — it also turns out that if you
are convinced that nobody could possibly like you, you
often become less inhibited. Not caring gives you a bul-
letproof aura of mystery and aloofness.

Complex Separation
The theory that, in music, a song gets only one chance
to make a first impression. After that the brain starts
breaking it down, subdividing the music experience into
its various components — lyrical, melodic, and so forth.

Connectopathy
Idiosyncratic behaviour that stems from idiosyncratic
neural connections.

Cover Buzz
The sensation felt when hearing a cover version of a
song one already knows.

Crazy Uncle Syndrome
Or, for that matter, Crazy Aunt Syndrome. One of the
few genuine indicators for success in life is having a few
crazy relatives. So long as you get only some of their
crazy genes, you don't end up crazy yourself — you
merely end up *different*. And it's that difference that

gives you an edge, that makes you successful. (See also Trainwreck Equilibration Theory)

Crystallographic Money Theory
The hypothesis that money is a crystallization or condensation of time and free will, the two characteristics that separate humans from other species. (See also Time/Will Uniqueness)

Dark-Age High Tech
Technical sophistication is relative. In the eleventh century, people who made steps leading up to their hovel doors were probably mocked as being high tech early adopters.

Deharmonized Sin
Seven deadly sins vs. the Ten Commandments vs. every other way of counting transgressions — the inability to scientifically count and calibrate sin.

Denarration
The process whereby one's life stops feeling like a story. (See also Limbic Trading; Narrative Drive; Sequential Dysphasia)

Deomiraculosteria
God's anger at always being asked to perform miracles.

Deromanticizing Dysfunction
Writes Alice Flaherty, "All the theories linking creativity to mental illness are really implying mild disease. People may be reassured by the fact that almost without exception no one is severely ill and still creative. Severe mental illness tends to bring bizarre preoccupation and inflexible thought. As the poet Sylvia Plath said, 'When you're insane, you're busy being insane — all the time when I was crazy, that's all I was.'"

Deselfing
Willingly diluting one's sense of self and ego by plastering the Internet with as much information as possible. (See also Omniscience Fatigue; Undeselfing)

Dimanchophobia
Fear of Sundays, not in a religious sense but, rather, a condition that reflects fear of unstructured time. Also known as acalendrical anxiety. Not to be confused with didominicaphobia or kyriakephobia, fear of the Lord's Day.

Dimanchophobia is a mental condition created by modernism and industrialism. Dimanchophobes particularly dislike the period between Christmas and New Year's, when days of the week lose their significance and time blurs into a perpetual Sunday. Another way of expressing dimanchophobia might be "life in a world without calendars." A popular expression of this condition can be found in the pop song "Every Day Is Like

Sunday," by Morrissey, in which he describes walking on a beach after a nuclear war, when every day of the week now feels like Sunday.

Drinking Your Own Spit
That's what it feels like to see yourself on TV.

Dummy Pronoun
The word *it*, as in "It's raining" or "It's six o'clock." Not to be confused with Itness. (See also Itness)

Ecosystemic Biology
Biology that looks at bodies, both human and animal, as ecosystems as opposed to discrete entities. This way of thinking is bolstered by the fact that the average body has roughly ten times as many outsider cells as it has of its own.

Eternal Divide
Unlike the future, Eternity, by its very definition, cannot be limited by the vagaries and unknowns of time. At best we can understand Eternity as existing outside of time, as timelessness — an infinite present. Which makes you rethink that eternal afterlife you were counting on. But don't worry, because another name for timelessness is nirvana. So it's all good.

Exosomatic Memory
Memory stored in externalized databases, which at

some point will exceed the amount of memory contained within our collective biological bodies. In other words, there will be more memory "out there" than exists inside all of us. As humans we will have peripheralized our essence.

Fate Is for Losers
A state of being whose opposite is Destiny Is for Winners.

Fictive Rest
The common inability of many people to be able to sleep until they have read even the tiniest amount of fiction. Although the element of routine is important at sleep time, reading fiction in bed allows another person's inner voice to hijack one's own, thus relaxing and lubricating the brain for sleep cycles. One booby trap, though: Don't finish your book before you fall asleep. Doing so miraculously keeps your brain whizzing for hours.

Field Denial
The near absence of any discussion around the fact that while fields exist (for example, magnetic fields) nobody actually knows how they work, nor are we any longer trying to figure them out.

Frankentime
What time feels like when you realize that most of your life is being spent working with and around a computer and the Internet. (See also Time Snack)

The Future of Labour

The fact that there is no word in the Chinese language for a "me day."

General Anesthetic Afterlife

The concept that death must be akin to being under general anesthetic. A variant of the belief that because you don't remember anything from before you were born, you need not worry about what happens after you die.

Goalpost Aura

The ability of places and objects, such as football goalposts or artwork in a museum, to possess an indescribable aura. An application of the more well-known process of sacralization — wherein places such as churches and mosques are understandably transformed through human emotion, thought, and belief into sacred places — to seemingly random elements of our lives.

Godseeking

An extreme version of Christmas Morning Feeling. Significant scientific literature has postulated that religious experience stems largely from a God module based in the temporal lobe. Additionally, for those who believe, as many physiatrists do, that our ideas of God are heavily influenced by our infant memories of giant, all-powerful beings — our parents — the hippocampus, encoder of those memories, must also be important for religious experience. And finally, there is evidence that the parietal lobe plays an important role in all mystical experience. All of which leads us to the primary objection to localizing religious activity in the brain, the reductionist "nothing but" argument: that if religious states are brain states, they are nothing but brain states, and the experience of God is simply a neurological phenomenon.

Grim Truth
You're smarter than TV. So what?

Guck Wonder
The brain has always been poorly understood. Warriors on ancient battlefields must have wondered what the grey guck was that spilled out when they lopped off the top of someone's skull. At least with a heart you could tell it was doing something useful. Maybe they saw the brain as filler material the gods used to fill skull cavities, the way pet food manufacturers bulk up tinned meat products with grains.

Humanalia
Things made by humans that exist only on earth and nowhere else in the universe. Examples include Teflon, NutraSweet, thalidomide, Paxil, and meaningfully sized chunks of element number 43, technetium.

Iddefodial Storage
The brain's way of protecting itself from itself. To whit, if our subconscious is so wonderful, why do our bodies work so hard to keep it deeply buried?

Ikeasis
The desire in both daily and consumer life to cling to generically designed objects. This need for clear, unconfusing forms is a means of simplifying life amid an onslaught of information. (See also Invariant Memory)

Indoor/Outdoor Voice
A very quick test one can use to understand the expressive world of people further along the autistic spectrum than others. People unable to modulate their voices to suit the environment are just that much further along. (See also Internal Voice Blindness; Preliterary Aural Bliss)

Inhibition Spectrum
From the centre to the right:
"normal" → shy → quiet → reclusive loner → scary loner → hermit → Unabomber

From the centre to the left:
"normal" → talkative → life of the party → no off button → rants → talks to self → madness

Instant Reincarnation
Most adults, no matter how great their life is, wish for

total radical change in their lives. The urge to reincarnate while still alive is near universal.

Internal Voice Blindness
The near universal inability of people to articulate the tone and personality of the voice that forms their interior monologue, a fact that undermines the conventional wisdom that one's inner voice is one's own. Witness the universal confusion when non-professionals hear recordings of their own voice. In fact, the tone of one's inner voice is almost impossible to nail down.

Curiously, what artists commonly refer to as their muse — a seemingly external voice that guides them in their work — is actually a defective and/or amplified inner voice mechanism, a function regulated by the brain's frontal and temporal lobes, which are responsible for speech and auditory processing.

Interruption-Driven Memory
We remember only the red traffic lights, never the green ones. The green ones keep us in the flow; the red ones interrupt and annoy us. Interruption: this accounts for the almost universal tendency of car drivers to be superstitious about stoplights.

Intraffinital Melancholy vs. Extraffinital Melancholy
Which is lonelier: to be single and lonely or to be lonely within a dead relationship?

Intravincular Familial Silence
We need to be around our families not because we have so many shared experiences to talk about, but because they know precisely which subjects to avoid.

Invariant Memory
The process whereby the brain determines when looking at an animal whether it is a dog or a cat. There exists no perfect model of a cat or a dog, yet we can instantly tell which is which by rapidly moving up and down long lists of traits that define cat-ness and dog-ness. The brain's ability to form invariant representations is the root of all intelligence. Some people refer to invariant memories as idealized Platonic forms or as generic forms.

Itness
The ability of one agent to create the perception of an object, person, or event as possessing "it" — for example, not wanting to be "it" in a game of tag — or even the ability of a dog owner to create instant itness when choosing a stick to be thrown for retrieval.

Karaokeal Amnesia
Most people don't know the complete lyrics of almost any song, particularly the ones they hold most dear. (See also Lyrical Putty)

Limbic Trading
The belief that the need for stories comes from deep

within the brain's limbic system — where memory and emotion percolate, and where stories are first processed before they are passed on to the left hemisphere, the home of intuition, imagination, and inspiration — and that storytelling is one limbic system's way of communicating with that of another person.

Limited Pool Romantic Theory
The belief that one can fall in love only a finite number of times, most commonly six.

Lyrical Putty
The lyrics one creates in one's head in the absence of knowing a song's real lyrics.

Malfactory Aversion
The ability to figure out what it is in life you don't do well, and then to stop doing it.

Mallproof Realms
Realms where shopping never happens. For example, *Star Trek* characters never go shopping. Also, universes that wilfully exclude commerce.

Mechanics of Friends and Influence
The fact that people will like and respect you for no other reason than that you give the illusion of remembering their names.

Me Goggles
The inability to accurately perceive ourselves as others do.

Memesphere
The realm of culturally tangible ideas.

Metaphor Blindness
An exceedingly common inability to understand metaphor, which often leads to avoidance of art forms, such as novels, where metaphor might be encountered. (See also Poetic Side Effects)

Metaphor Spectrum
Confusion in the noun centre of the brain that leads to schizophrenic or delusional thinking:

Napoleon was a general → Napoleon is great → I think I am great → I am Napoleon

Monophobia
Dislike of feeling like an individual.

Nanoexploitative Industry
Pretty much everything invented after the year 1900 is based on our knowledge of things that are incredibly tiny and processes that occur at atomic or subatomic levels.

Narrative Drive
The belief that a life without a story is a life not worth

living — quite common, and ironically accompanied by the fact that most people cannot ascribe a story to their lives.

Negative Nonprocessing
The fact that the brain doesn't process negatives. Try *not* thinking of peeling an orange. Try not imagining the juice running down your fingers, the soft inner part of the peel, the smell. Try — you can't.

Next-Flight-Homers
People who click on the Internet but not in real life when they go to meet their hookup at an airport cocktail lounge; related to but not the same as Room-Getters — people who click both on the Internet and in real life.

Ninetenicillin
A pill that makes one feel as if the events of 9/11 had never occurred. A variation of Millennial Tristesse, a longing for the twentieth century.

Nonrotational Dreamlessness
The theory that dreams are largely a biological response to the planet's rotation, so citizens of planets that do not rotate most likely do not dream.

Noun-Nouning
By repeating a noun twice, one invokes the noun's generic form, its invariant-memory form. "No, I don't

want blue khakis with pleats. Just give me clean generic beige khaki-khakis." Or, "Officer, I've tried to remember what kind of car the getaway car was but I can't — it was just a car-car."

Omniscience Fatigue
The burnout that comes with being able to know the answer to almost anything online.

Omnislut
Mitochondrial Eve — the "universal mother" — a female who lived about 200,000 years ago, to whom all human beings are related via the mitochondrial DNA pathway. "Superdog," a.k.a. Y-Chromosomal Adam, the universal father, lived 60,000 years ago.

Pathologography
A new strain of biographical writing that acknowledges the importance of performing forensic analysis of the subject's physical and mental states. Biology is not destiny, but it can certainly open and close a few doors.

Permanent Halloween
The ultimate expression of individuality is to arrive at a point where one wears a Halloween costume every day of the year. Writes Louise Adler, "The more like ourselves we become, the odder we become. This is most obvious in people whom society no longer keeps in line; the eccentricity of the very rich or of castaways."

Phantom Point

An object that exists but, when you really think about it, does not; for example, a corner or an edge. Also known as "virtual tangibles," phantom points must be considered when contemplating theoretical geometry. For example, the head of a pin — a point that obviously exists and yet does not — is theoretically no different than the state of the universe before the Big Bang. It encompasses everything and nothing.

Poetic Side Effects

The result of looking at a water molecule and being able to predict rainbows, or inventing the motor vehicle and predicting that dogs will cheerfully stick their faces out into the oncoming wind.

Point Mesmerization

Deflection by dispersion. The manner in which a lion tamer controls a lion, keeping it mesmerized by holding a chair up to its face, legs first. The lion, unable to relinquish its instinctual and powerful ability to focus, stares at the ends of the chair legs, its eyes darting back and forth between the four of them to the exclusion of the larger picture.

Polydexterity

Handedness isn't just about writing or throwing a ball. It can be applied to almost all body activities: winking, crossing the legs, guitar playing, sleeping on one's side, and so forth. No person is ever universally monodextrous.

Pope Gregory's Day-timer

Doesn't mean anything in particular, but it certainly would have been interesting to see.

Post-adolescent Expert Syndrome

The tendency of young people around the age of eighteen, males especially, to become altruistic experts on everything, a state of mind required by nature to ensure warriors who are willing to die with pleasure on the battlefield. Also the reason why religions recruit kamikaze pilots and suicide bombers almost exclusively from the 18-to-21 age range. "Kyle, I never would have guessed that when you were up in your bedroom playing World of Warcraft all through your teens, you were, in fact, becoming an expert on the films of Jean-Luc Godard."

The inability of teens to consider the consequences of risky action is due to the fact that their brain's development is only 80 percent finished. The cortex matures from back to front, leaving connection and development of the frontal lobe incomplete until somewhere in the mid to late twenties. Not surprisingly, the frontal lobe is home to reasoning, planning, and judgement.

Post-human

Whatever it is that we become next.

Preliterary Aural Bliss
The notion that what you think of as your inner voice is actually a rather new "invention" created by the printed word, solitary reading, and a text-mediated daily environment. In the old days — say, a thousand years ago — people didn't have an inner voice. Citizens inhabited a mental universe that had more to do with sound effects than speech. Words and voices might pass through your head, but it wasn't necessarily *you* that was speaking. Maybe the king or the gods or something, but not you.

Proceleration
The acceleration of acceleration.

Propanolol
A beta blocker used by the military that curtails adrenaline production, which in turn reduces memory production, which in turn reduces post-traumatic stress.

Proscenial Universe Theory
The notion that time simply provides a medium — an arena — within which emotions are able to play themselves out. As Joyce Carol Oates says, "Time is the element in which we exist. We are either borne along by it or drowned in it."

Proteinic Inevitability
The tendency for life-forming molecules to aggregate and create life the first moment they possibly can. So

dedicated are they to this cause, recent research suggests that in the beginning stages of life on earth, small molecules acted as "molecular midwives," assisting in the formation of life-creating polymers and appropriate selection of base pairs for the DNA double helix.

Pseudoalienation
The inability of humans to create genuinely alienating situations. Anything made by humans is a de facto expression of humanity. Technology cannot be alienating because humans created it. Genuinely alien technologies can be created only by aliens. Technically, a situation one might describe as alienating is, in fact, "humanating."

Punning Syndrome
The medicalization of what was previously considered merely an annoying verbal tic displayed by a limited number of people. Punning is an almost inevitable side effect of connectopathies within the brain's verbal nodes, somewhat akin to Tourette syndrome.

This leads to a larger discussion about the concept of spectrum behaviour: sliding scales of behaviour connected by clinical appearance and underlying causation, ranging from mild clinical deficits to severe disorder. Psychiatric disorders understood along spectrums include autism, paranoia, obsessive compulsion, anxiety, and conditions that result from congenital malformations, brain damage, and aging. There are many more, however, and each category itself can be broken down into more specific spectrums.

Quantum-DNA Link Theory

The belief that DNA is not just a blueprint or recipe for life, but that the physical DNA molecule acts as a quantum-level transmitter or homing device communicating with other life-forming molecules in the universe — similar molecules that act as blueprints for other sentient beings that are aware of space and time and the role of themselves within it. This theory presupposes that countless sentient beings exist throughout the universe, and that life is the universe's raison d'être. It is a lot to believe in, but ultimately this line of thought resonates with swaths of belief systems, from "the Buddhist concept of Indra's net, Teilhard de Chardin's conception of the noosphere, James Lovelock's Gaia theory, to Hegel's Absolute idealism, Satori in Zen, and to some traditional pantheist beliefs. It is also reminiscent of Carl Jung's collective unconscious." Thank you, Wikipedia.

Random Sequence Buzz

The small, pleasant chemical reaction experienced in the brain when hearing the next song in a randomly sequenced finite song list. Not to be confused with radio sequence buzz, wherein songs are drawn from a reasonably well defined yet still open-ended supply of music.

Rapture Goo

The stuff that gets left behind. The fact that the only thing that really defines you is your DNA. Jesus gets your DNA. That's all he gets, roughly 7.6 milligrams of *you*. All the blood and guts and bones and undigested food and everything else within the ecosystem that is your body will simply grace the floor.

Red Queen's Blog Syndrome

The more one races onto one's blog to assert one's uniqueness, the more generic one becomes.

Romantic Superstition

Dislike of having the romantic notion of personality reduced to a set of brain and body functions.

Rosenwald's Theorem

The belief that all the wrong people have self-esteem.

Sequential Dysphasia

Dysfunctional mental states do stem from malfunctions in the brain's sequencing capacity. One commonly known short-term sequencing dysfunction is dyslexia. People unable to sequence over a slightly longer term might be "no good with directions." The ultimate sequencing dysfunction is the inability to look at one's life as a meaningful sequence or story.

Sequential Thinking
The ability to create and remember sequences is an almost entirely human ability (some crows have been shown to sequence). Dogs, while highly intelligent, still cannot form sequences; it's the reason why the competitors at dog sports shows are led from station to station by handlers instead of completing the course themselves.

Sin Fatigue
When hearing about the sins of others ceases to be compelling, a condition most commonly experienced by religious and medical professionals.

Situational Disinhibition
A social contrivance within which one is allowed to become disinhibited, that is, a moment of culturally approved disinhibition. This occurs when speaking with fortune tellers, to dogs and other pets, to strangers and bartenders in bars, or with Ouija boards.

The Social Question
If you were to jump off the Golden Gate Bridge, would you do it facing the city or facing the ocean? In answering, one is forced to wonder about the absolute extent to which social behaviour is embedded in the human psyche. "True suicides" don't care what side of the bridge they jump from. If one gets up there and considers the

question "Do I face the city or the Pacific Ocean?" then the implication is that the suicide attempt is not a hundred percent genuine.

Somnimural Release
The ability of dreams to prevent you from remembering that the dead are dead, or that vanished friends have vanished.

Somnitropic Drugs
Drugs engineered to affect one's dream life.

Standard Deviation
Feeling unique is no indication of uniqueness, yet it is the feeling of uniqueness that convinces us we have souls.

Star Shock
The disproportionate way in which meeting a celebrity feels slightly like being told a piece of life-changing news.

Stovulax
A micro-targeted drug of the future designed to stop fantastically specific OCD cases, in this case a compulsion involving the inability of some people to convince themselves after leaving the house that the stove is turned off. As science further maps the brain, such micro-targeted drugs become ever more plausible.

Technological Fatalism

An attitude positing that the next sets of triumphing technologies are going to happen no matter who invents them or where or how. The only unknown factor is the pace at which they will appear.

Time Lance

Suppose one could send a particle a millionth of a second ahead in the future. By knowing its direction and speed, one could then determine the net overall expansion direction and speed of the universe.

Time Snack

Often annoying moments of pseudo-leisure created by computers when they stop responding in order to save a file, to search for software updates, or, most likely, for no apparent reason.

Time/Will Uniqueness

The belief that awareness of time and the possession of free will are the only two characteristics that separate humans from all other creatures.

Torn-Paper Geography

The phenomenon in which, if you take a sheet of paper and rip it in half, both pieces will probably resemble an American state or Canadian province. If one contin-ues to rip the paper, the phenomenon continues — a reflection of New World geopolitics versus the Old

World. European and Asian borders are delineated by rivers, watersheds, and battlefields. New World borders are most often a mixture of rivers and the nineteenth-century Cartesian grid. Old World = people before property; New World = property before people.

Trainwreck Equilibration Theory
The belief that in the end, every family experiences an equal amount of trials, disorders, quirks, and medical dilemmas. One family might get more cancer, another might be more bipolar or schizo, but in the end it all averages out into one big train wreck per family.

Trans-human
Whatever technology made by humans that ends up becoming smarter than humans.

Trans-humane Conundrum
If technology is only a manifestation of our intrinsic humanity, how can we possibly make something smarter than ourselves?

Trigenerational Amnesia
The reluctance of most people to investigate their family tree back more than three or four generations. There are more reasons for not wanting to know than to know. Too much research could possibly destabilize one's beliefs about oneself, beliefs that may or may not be correct.

Unchecked

"Unchecked, science and monotheism both mean to vanquish nature" — a lovely quote from Christopher Potter in *You Are Here: A Portable History of the Universe*.

Undeselfing

The attempt, usually frantic and futile, to reverse the deselfing process.

Universal Sentience

The notion that apprehension of the universe by humans or other intelligence is, in a fundamental sense, the universe's raison d'être.

Unwitting Permanence

The notion that when you, say, throw a Coke bottle off a ship's deck to the bottom of the Marianas Trench, that bottle will remain there, unambiguously, until the sun eats up the planet. Most of the world's landfills display unwitting permanence.

Vision Dysphasia

The counterintuitive manner in which people born blind, given vision later in life through medical advances, tend to very much dislike that vision.

Weather Test

If human beings had never existed, would the weather outside your window right now be exactly the same?

Of course not. So we've obviously changed things. So it becomes an issue of figuring out how different the earth would have been minus human beings.

Web-Emergent Sentience Theory
The belief that globally linked computer systems will one day erupt into some new form of overriding post-human sentience. Sometimes referred to as singularity.

Web Sentience Release
The belief that this newly evolved web sentience will relieve people of the crushing need to be individual.

Why We Keep Our Distance
Once you've seen a person go psycho, you can never look at him or her the same way ever again.

Witness Elimination Program
The myth is that witness relocation exists, whereas people who "enter the program" are simply shot.

Zoosomnial Blurring
The notion that animals probably don't see much difference between dreaming and being awake.

This novel comprises the 2010 Massey Lectures, broadcast in Canada in November 2010 as part of CBC Radio's Ideas series. The series was created in honour of the Right Honourable Vincent Massey, former Governor General of Canada, and was inaugurated in 1961 to provide a forum on radio where major contemporary thinkers could address important issues of our time.

The Massey Lectures are co-sponsored by CBC Radio, House of Anansi Press, and Massey College in the University of Toronto.